Welcome to the Wonderful World of

Geography

WORLD PHYSICAL GEOGRAPHY

Teacher's Guide

TABLE OF CONTENTS

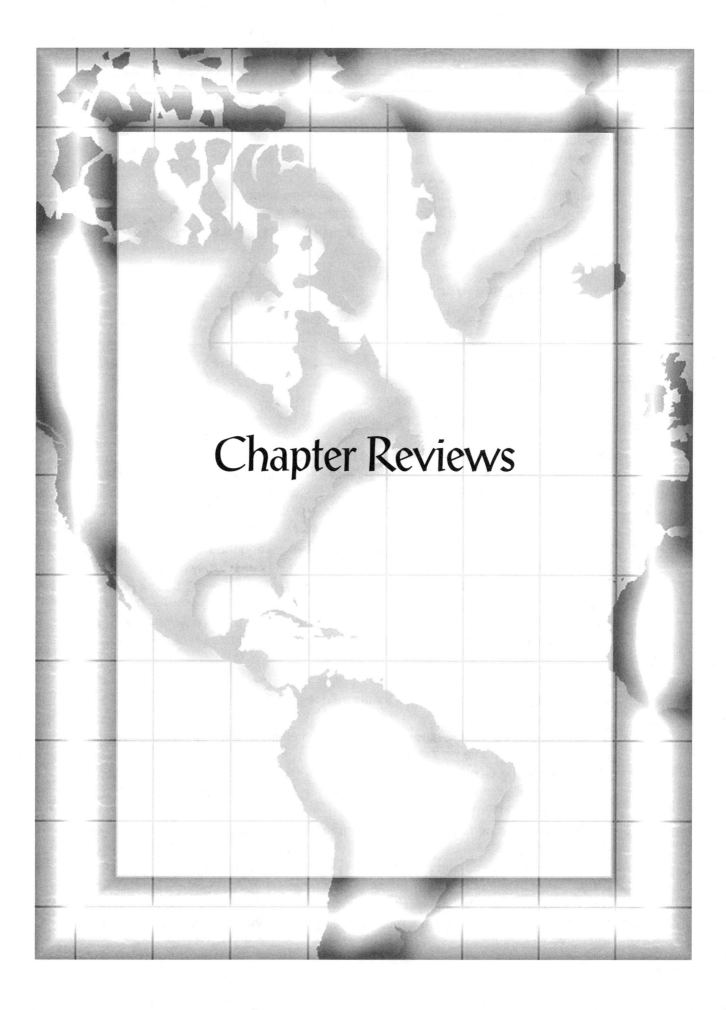

Chapter Reviews

Chapter 1 Review   Our Planet Earth

LESSON 1

REVIEW STATEMENTS
1. The earth is in the Milky Way galaxy.
2. There are nine planets in the solar system.
3. The sun is a star and the source of heat for the entire solar system.
4. Mercury, Venus, Earth, and Mars are terrestrial planets and made of rock.
5. Jupiter, Saturn, Uranus, and Neptune are Jovian planets and are made of frozen gases.
6. Pluto is classified as neither terrestrial nor Jovian.

REVIEW QUESTIONS (PAGE 6)
1. The earth is in which galaxy?
   The Milky Way.
2. List the terrestrial planets.
   Mercury, Venus, Earth, and Mars.
3. List the Jovian planets.
   Jupiter, Saturn, Uranus, and Neptune.
4. What planet is neither terrestrial nor Jovian?
   Pluto.
5. What is the difference between terrestrial and Jovian planets?
   Terrestrial planets are relatively small and dense, and consist of rock material believed to be similar to that of the earth. They have very few if any moons. Jovian planets are made of frozen gases, such as methane and ammonia, and are much less dense than terrestrial planets. Each of these planets has several moons as well as distinctive rings of particles.
6. Our solar system is held together by push-pull forces. Using the words push and pull discuss how centrifugal force maintains the balance of our solar system.
   The sun acts like a giant magnet pulling the planets toward itself. As the planets orbit or move in a curved motion around the sun, centrifugal force pushes them away from the center of the curve, which is the sun. The push of centrifugal force and the pull of the sun strike a balance, keeping the planets from being pulled into the sun or flying into space.

VOCABULARY
1. **star:** a large, luminous ball of gas that is held together by its own gravity.
2. **universe:** all that exists.
3. **galaxy:** one of the vast numbers of systems containing stars, nebulae, star clusters and space debris that make up the universe.
4. **Milky Way:** our galaxy.
5. **light year:** the distance light travels in a vacuum in one year, approximately 5.88 trillion miles (9.46 trillion km).
6. **satellite:** a man-made object or vehicle made to orbit the earth; a celestial body orbiting another of larger size.
7. **solar system:** the sun and everything that orbits around the sun.
8. **orbit:** the path taken by a body in space as it moves around its center of attraction.
9. **revolution:** a complete turn around an axis or point.
10. **centrifugal force:** the force that moves objects in a curved motion away from the center of the curve.

11. **axis:** an imaginary pole that passes through the earth, connecting the North and South Poles.
12. **circle of illumination:** the zone of transition between light and dark around a sphere.
13. **terrestrial planets:** planets composed of rock material similar to Earth's.
14. **Jovian planets:** planets composed of frozen gases.
15. **asteroid:** a celestial body that is a few feet to several hundred miles across and has a distinct orbit.

LESSON 2

REVIEW STATEMENTS
1. The seven continents are Asia, Africa, North America, South America, Antarctica, Europe, and Australia.
2. Greenland is the largest island.
3. The cardinal directions are north, east, south, and west.
4. The intermediate directions are northeast, southeast, southwest, and northwest.

REVIEW QUESTIONS (PAGE 10)
1. List the seven continents from the largest to the smallest.
    Asia, Africa, North America, South America, Antarctica, Europe, and Australia.
2. List the three largest islands from the largest to the smallest.
    Greenland, New Guinea, and Borneo.
3. List the cardinal directions.
    The cardinal directions are north, east, south, and west.
4. List the intermediate directions.
    The intermediate directions are northeast, southeast, southwest, and northwest.
5. In your opinion, should Greenland become the eighth continent or should it remain just an island? Explain your answer, please.

VOCABULARY
1. **continent:** one of the seven principle landmasses on earth.
2. **island:** any land mass smaller than a continent that is completely surrounded by water.
3. **cardinal directions:** the four primary directions: north, east, south, and west.
4. **intermediate directions:** the four directions that fall between the four primary directions: northeast, southeast, southwest, and northwest.
5. **compass rose:** a diagram that shows the directions in relation to each other.

LESSON 3

REVIEW STATEMENTS
1. Relative location refers to where something is in relation to another object.
2. Europe and Asia combine to form Eurasia.
3. North America lies northwest of South America.
4. You can only go north from the center of Antarctica.

REVIEW QUESTIONS (PAGE 14)

1. List the nine planets.

    Mercury, Venus, Earth, Mars, Jupiter, Saturn, Uranus, Neptune, and Pluto.

2. List the seven continents from the largest to the smallest.

    Asia, Africa, North America, South America, Antarctica, Europe, and Australia.

3. Which two continents appear to be one?

    Europe and Asia appear to be one continent.

4. Which continent is closest to Antarctica?

    South America.

5. Which continent is closest to North America?

    Asia or South America. The traditional answer is Asia, but because South America is connected to North America via Central America, it is literally closer.

6. Which continent has a "horn"?

    Africa

7. Where does North America lie in relation to South America?

    North America is northwest of South America.

8. What body of water separates Africa from Europe?

    The Mediterranean Sea.

9. How far is Spain from Morocco at the Strait of Gibraltar?

    Spain is 8 miles from Morocco at the Strait of Gibraltar.

10. What is the relationship between Australia and India?

    They are located on the same plate, and wherever India goes Australia has to follow.

11. You are a penguin living on the South Pole in Antarctica. There are windows on each wall in your house: front, back, and side windows. Which window would you look out to look north? Discuss why.

    Any window you look out will face north. This is because from the South Pole there is only one way to go, North!

VOCABULARY

1. **relative location:** where something is in relation to another object.
2. **plates:** huge rigid slabs of crust
3. **compass:** an instrument with a magnetic needle that spins to align itself with the earth's magnetic poles.

LESSON 4

REVIEW STATEMENTS

1. The five oceans are the Pacific, Atlantic, Arctic, Antarctic, and Indian Oceans.
2. The oceans cover over 70% of the earth's surface.
3. The Pacific is the largest ocean.
4. Oceanographers are people who study oceans.

REVIEW QUESTIONS (PAGE *17*)

1. List the three largest islands from largest to smallest.
   Greenland, New Guinea, and Borneo.
2. Which continent has a "horn"?
   Africa.
3. List the "seven seas."
   The North Atlantic, South Atlantic, North Pacific, South Pacific, Arctic, Antarctic and Indian Oceans.
4. List the five major oceans from the largest to the smallest. Why are there five oceans and not seven?
   Pacific, Atlantic, Indian, Arctic, and Antarctic. There are only five major oceans because we no longer separate the Pacific and Atlantic Oceans into north and south sections.
5. What is the name of the sea near the middle of the Atlantic Ocean?
   The Sargasso Sea.
6. List three facts about the North Atlantic Drift (Gulf Stream).
   It carries 5,000 times as much water as the Mississippi River. It is 13,000 miles around. It can move a drifting boat one hundred miles north in one day.
7. List four facts about the Pacific Ocean.
   It is the largest ocean, covering roughly one third of the earth's surface. It is twice as big and has more than twice as much water as the Atlantic. It covers more surface area than all the land on earth. The Pacific is shrinking. It is separated from the Arctic Ocean in the north by the Bering Strait.
8. Why is the water warmer in the North Pacific than in the South Pacific?
   Because there is more land in the Northern Hemisphere than in the Southern Hemisphere, and land warms much faster than water. Furthermore, the land in the south is the frozen continent of Antarctica.
9. List three facts about the Atlantic Ocean.
   It is the second largest ocean and covers roughly one fifth of the world. It lies between Europe and North America, and between Africa and South America. It is neither as deep as the Pacific nor as cold. It is getting bigger as the continents on either side of it move farther apart.
10. List the smaller bodies of water that are included as part of the Indian Ocean.
    The Red Sea and the Persian Gulf.
11. What keeps Antarctica the "frozen continent"?
    A single current of cold water completely encircles Antarctica preventing warm waters from reaching its shores.

VOCABULARY

1. **ocean:** the body of salt water that covers over 70% of the earth's surface and is divided into five primary oceans.
2. **sea:** a body of water smaller than an ocean.
3. **salinity:** the amount of salt contained in a solution.
4. **oceanographer:** one who studies oceans.

Chapter 2 Review   Maps and Their Uses

LESSON 5

REVIEW STATEMENTS
1. A three-dimensional globe is the most accurate representation of the earth.
2. A two-dimensional map or projection is the representation of the earth on a flat piece of paper.
3. The only true map of Antarctica is an azimuthal polar projection.
4. The 180° meridian of longitude and the prime meridian together make a great circle.
5. All maps or projections show some sort of distortion.
6. A cartographer is a person who draws maps.
7 A great circle is any imaginary line that divides the earth into two equal parts.
8. A great circle route is the path traveled between any two point on a great circle.
9. A great circle route is always the shortest way to go.
10. Mercator, azimuthal, Goode, Robinson and Winkel are examples of different map projections.

REVIEW QUESTIONS (PAGE 27)
1. List the five major oceans.
    Pacific, Atlantic, Indian, Arctic, and Antarctic.
2. List the seven continents.
    Asia, Africa, North America, South America, Antarctica, Europe, and Australia.
3. List the cardinal and intermediate directions.
    North, northeast, east, southeast, south, southwest, west, and northwest.
4. What problems do cartographers face in drawing a map of the earth?
    Drawing a three-dimensional object on a two-dimensional piece of paper. Deciding whether to draw accurate shape, size, distance, or direction.
5. How is the Mercator map distorted?
    The size of the land masses become more distorted as you move from the equator toward the poles. For example, on a Mercator map Greenland appears much larger than it actually is.
6. How is a polar projection limited in its use?
    It can only be used to see either the Southern or Northern Hemisphere at one time. It won't allow you to see all of the Eastern or Western Hemispheres at one time.
7. What is unusual about a Goode projection and why is it difficult to use?
    It is unusual for a map because it shows fairly accurate sizes and shapes, but it is difficult to use because it is divided into sections. It is difficult to measure accurate distances across the different pieces of the map.
8. How can you recognize a Robinson projection?
    One way to recognize a Robinson is by the size and shape of the distortion in the polar areas. It is also rounded on the sides and flat on top and bottom.
9. Which map projection will give you the true shape of Antarctica?
    A polar projection gives the true shape of Antarctica.
10. Which projection will give you the true proportions of land and water?
    The Goode projection gives true proportions of land and water.
11. Which projection is conformal?
    The Mercator projection is conformal.

12. Why is a globe the most accurate representation of the earth?

   It is a three dimensional object that can show the height, width, and depth of the earth accurately.

13. Where does distortion become the greatest on a map?

   Distortion is greatest near the edges of a map.

14. Why is a Great Circle route the shortest distance between two places on Earth?

   A great circle route plots the shortest distance between two places based upon the curvature of the earth.

15. Match the shape of Greenland with the correct projection:

   I. Mercator - A

   II. Polar - C

   III. Goode Interrupted - D

   IV. Robinson - B

   V. Winkel Tripel - E

A.    B.    C.   D.    E.

Vocabulary

1. **quest**: a search or pursuit made in order to find or obtain something.
2. **three-dimensional object**: an object with height, width, and depth.
3. **cartographer**: a person who draws maps.
4. **simultaneously**: occurring at the same time.
5. **projection**: a system by which lines of latitude and longitude are drawn onto a planar surface so as to represent the curved surface of the earth.
6. **compromise**: an agreement reached where those involved give up something.
7. **Gerhardus Mercator**: the first cartographer to name both North and South America. Mercator maps have accurate shapes but inaccurate size.
8. **distortion**: the state of being twisted or stretched out of shape.
9. **conformal map**: a map that maintains the true shapes of land masses but not the sizes. Lines of longitude and latitude will cross at right angles as they do on a globe. The Mercator is a conformal map.
10. **azimuthal projection**: a circular projection that shows one-half of the globe. Distances on an azimuthal accurately reflect the curved surface of the earth.
11. **hemisphere:** half of a sphere or globe
12. **polar projection**: an azimuthal projection that is centered on one of the poles.
13. **great circle**: any imaginary line that circles the earth and divides it into two equal parts.
14. **great circle route**: travel between any two points along a great circle.
15. **Goode projection**: a projection of the earth in which certain portions of the oceans are removed to lessen distortion.
16. **Robinson projection**: a projection that maintains the overall shape and relative positions without extreme distortion. Most classrooms use this projection.
17. **Winkel Tripel**: an oval projection that maintains realistic shapes with minor size distortions at all latitudes.
18. **ice sheet**: an extensive continuous area of land ice.
19. **ice shelf**: a large sheet of ice extending from land over the surrounding sea.

20. **iceberg:** a huge mass of floating ice that breaks off an ice shelf or the end of a glacier. Most of the ice is underwater.

21. **ice floe:** a mass of ice that breaks off from larger ice bodies and floats freely in the sea. Its surface is flat.

22. **ice pack:** an extensive, cohesive mass of floating ice found in the Arctic and Antarctic Oceans.

CRITICAL THINKING ACTIVITY: GREAT CIRCLE ROUTES (PAGE 28)

1. What is the great circle distance between Paris, France and Beirut, Lebanon?
   1,986 miles

2. What is the great circle distance between Paris and Seoul, South Korea?
   5,579 miles

3. Which city is farthest from Seattle, Washington by the great circle route? What is the closest city?
   Madras is the farthest. Paris is the closest.

4. Which city is closest to Madras, India? Which is farthest?
   Beirut is the closest. Seattle is the farthest.

5. Which ocean would you fly over going from Seattle, Washington to Madras, India, using the great circle route?
   The Arctic Ocean.

6. Which two cities are the farthest apart? Which two cities are closest?
   Seattle and Madras are the farthest apart. Istanbul and Beirut are the closest.

7. Which ocean would you fly over between Seattle and Moscow, Russia?
   The Arctic Ocean.

8. If you flew the great circle route from Madrid, Spain to Madras, India, which city would you fly over?
   Beirut

9. Which great circle route flies over the Atlantic Ocean?
   The Seattle to Madrid route.

10. Which route flies over China and Russia?
    The Seoul to Paris route.

LESSON 6

CRITICAL THINKING ACTIVITY: A WALKING TOUR OF WASHINGTON D.C. (PAGES 33-35)

A. 3 - White House
B. 7 - U.S. Holocaust Memorial Museum
C. 8 - Bureau of Engraving and Printing
D. 5 - National Museum of American History
E. 4 - Justice Department
F. 11 - IRS, Internal Revenue Service
G. 14 - Ford's Theatre
H. 6 - National Air and Space Museum
I. 1 - Department of Agriculture
J. 9 -Vietnam Veterans Memorial
K. 13 - Washington Monument
L. 2 - Lincoln Memorial
M. 10 - General Services Administration
N. 12 - The Ellipse

REVIEW STATEMENTS

1. The five basic parts of a map are: title, legend, grid system, direction, and scale.
2. A large scale map shows a large amount of detail about a small area (e.g., a map of a neighborhood).
3. A small scale map shows a small amount of detail about a large area (e.g., a map of the world).

REVIEW QUESTIONS (PAGE 36)

1. List the nine planets.
   Mercury, Venus, Earth, Mars, Jupiter, Saturn, Uranus, Neptune, and Pluto.
2. Where does distortion become greatest on a map?
   Distortion is greatest near the edges of a map.
3. What body of water separates Africa from Europe?
   The Mediterranean Sea.
4. List the five major parts of a map and define each one.
   Title: tells the reader the subject of the map.
   Legend: shows colors, patterns, or symbols used on the map and what they represent.
   Grid System: the interlocking set of lines established by parallels of latitude and meridians of longitude which is used to find an exact location.
   Direction: shows the cardinal and/or intermediate directions on the map
   Scale: shows the size relationship of the items on the map using a representative fraction.
5. What does a large scale map show? Give an example.
   A large scale map shows a large amount of detail about a small area. An example is a map of my neighborhood.
6. What does a small scale map show? Give an example.
   A small scale map shows a small amount of detail about a large area. An example is a map of the continents of the world.

VOCABULARY

1. **legend:** the part of a map showing colors, patterns or symbols and what they represent.
2. **scale:** the relationship between size on a map and size of an actual object.
3. **large scale** : showing a large amount of detail about a small area.
4. **small scale**: showing a small amount of detail about a large area.

LESSON 7

CRITICAL THINKING ACTIVITY (PAGE 38)

If you are 5'6" tall, you are five feet and six inches tall. How many meters tall are you?
First convert to inches. 5' x 12" (inches per foot) = 60" + 6" = 66" tall. Since there are 25.4 millimeters in an inch, multiply 66" by 25.4 mm. The answer is 1676.4 millimeters which converts to 1.676 meters tall.

Here is a chart to show you how to move your decimal points in the metric system:

kilometers	meters	decimeters	centimeters	millimeters
1,000	1	.1	.01	.001

How many centimeters tall are you? How many decimeters?
   You are 167.64 centimeters tall and 16.764 decimeters tall.

CRITICAL THINKING ACTIVITY (PAGE 39)

Determine the distances between: (Your answers should be close to these figures.)

1. Boston, Massachusetts and Chicago, Illinois   *870 miles (1,400 km)*
2. Detroit, Michigan and Los Angeles, California   *1,955 miles (3,146 km)*
3. Miami, Florida and Seattle, Washington   *2,670 miles (4,297 km)*
4. Bismarck, North Dakota and Houston, Texas   *1,200 miles (1,931 km)*
5. New Orleans, Louisiana and Nashville, Tennessee   *480 miles (772 km)*
6. Santa Fe, New Mexico and Oklahoma City, Oklahoma   *480 miles (772 km)*
7. San Francisco, California and Salem, Oregon   *460 miles (740 km)*

Is it possible to determine the distance between New York City, New York and Honolulu, Hawaii using this map?

     No

CRITICAL THINKING ACTIVITY (PAGE 40)

Practice (Your answers should be close to these figures.)

1. How far is it from Los Angeles to Bismarck in miles and kilometers? (See Fig. 2-27)

     1289 miles (2074 km)

2. How far is it from Nashville to Washington D.C.? (See Fig. 2-27) Again, give your answer in both kilometers and miles.

     541 miles (871 km)

3. Which two cities are the farthest apart?

     Seattle and Miami

Practice (Your answers should be close to these figures.)

4. If you traveled from New Orleans, Louisiana to Santa Fe, New Mexico, which direction would you be going and how many miles would you travel? If you drove 55 m.p.h., how long would it take you to get there? (Distance divided by m.p.h. will give you the number of hours.)

     You would drive northwest and travel 976 miles. You would drive 17.75 hours.

5. If you get only 15 miles to the gallon, how much gas will you use? (Divide distance by the miles per gallon.)

     You would use 65 gallons of gas.

MAP ACTIVITY (PAGE 41)

You have just landed at the International Airport in Rio de Janeiro, Brazil. You are staying at the Meridian Hotel on Copacabana Beach. Please answer the following questions using the bar scale on the left. (Your answers should be close to these figures.)

1. After landing at the airport, you must take a taxi to your hotel. How many kilometers must you travel to reach the hotel? Be sure to follow the streets marked red.

     32 km

2. One kilometer is equal to .62 miles. How far is the drive from the airport in miles?

     19.84 miles

3. Sugar Loaf is the name of the huge dome shaped rocks which are one of the most recognizable physical features in Brazil. If you are at your hotel and want to visit Sugar Loaf, which direction would you travel?

     Northeast

4. Rio de Janeiro is home to the largest soccer stadium in the world, Maracana. It holds 180,000 fans. Two of Rio's top teams, Flamengo and Vasco, are playing. How many miles is it from your hotel to the stadium? One mile is equal to 1.609 kilometers. How many kilometers would you travel?

    8.5 miles (13.7 km)

5. The weather is beautiful. Let's go to the beach. Ipanema Beach is too crowded, so you decide to go to a less well-known, but beautiful beach across the Rio-Niteroi bridge. How long is the bridge in kilometers?

    9.8 km

6. The money system in the U.S. is based on the dollar. The money system in Brazil is based on the real (pronounced "hey-al"). A taxi costs .85 reals per km. How much would it cost to travel across the Rio-Niteroi bridge?

    9.8 km multiplied by .85 = 8.33 reals

REVIEW STATEMENTS
1. The French developed the metric system.
2. The metric system is based on the number 10.
3. There are 10 decimeters in a meter.
4. There are 10 centimeters in a decimeter.

REVIEW QUESTIONS (PAGE 42)
1. The earth is in which galaxy?
    The Milky Way.
2. List the five major oceans.
    Pacific, Atlantic, Indian, Arctic, and Antarctic.
3. Why is a globe the most accurate representation of Earth?
    It is a three-dimensional object that can show the height, width, and depth of the earth accurately.
4. What country developed the metric system?
    France developed the metric system.
5. The metric unit is based upon what number unit?
    10
6. One meter equals how many inches?
    39.37 inches
7. Seventy-eight miles equal how many kilometers?
    125.5 km

THERE ARE NO LESSON 7 VOCABULARY WORDS.

Chapter 3 Review   Latitude and Climate

LESSON 8

REVIEW STATEMENTS
1. The equator divides the earth into halves.
2. *Hemi-* means "half"; a hemisphere is half a sphere or globe.
3. A hemisphere is half a sphere or globe.
4. Parallel lines never cross.
5. Parallels of latitude measure the distance north or south of the equator.
6. Parallels of latitude are measured in degrees, not feet or miles.
7. The equator is at 0° latitude.
8. The North Pole is at 90° N latitude; the South Pole is at 90° S latitude.

REVIEW QUESTIONS (PAGE 46)
1. Two hundred inches equals how many meters?
    5.08 meters
2. The metric system is based upon what number unit?
    10
3. What is relative location?
    Relative location is where something is in relation to another object.
4. What is the difference between a large scale and small scale map?
    A large scale map shows a large amount of detail over a small area and a small scale map shows a small amount of detail over a large area.
5. What terms do geographers use to indicate direction?
    Geographers use the cardinal directions: north, south, east and west.
6. What is the numerical value of the equator's latitude?
    0°

VOCABULARY WORDS
1. **equator**: a great circle that divides the earth into halves forming the Northern and Southern Hemispheres.
2. **hemisphere**: half a sphere or globe.
3. **parallel**: remaining an equal distance apart at all times and at all points.
4. **latitude**: distance north or south of the equator.
5. **North Pole**: 90° north latitude; the northernmost point on the globe.
6. **South Pole**: 90° south latitude, the southernmost point on the globe.

LESSON 9

HANDS-ON ACTIVITY (PAGE 49)   *Note: Only items 5 and 7 ask questions.*
5. Estimate where 23.5° should be and draw a dotted line north of the equator and another dotted line south of the equator. What is the climate between the two dotted lines?
    It will be hot year-round.
7. Draw lines at 66.5° N and S and label them the Arctic Circle in the north and the Antarctic Circle in the south. What is the importance of these lines? What is the temperature in this region?
    These lines mark the edge of an area where the sun stays above the horizon one or more days each year. The temperature in this area will be cold year-round.

REVIEW STATEMENTS
1. The direct rays of the sun fall on the tropics, between 23.5° N and 23.5° S latitude.
2. The low latitudes are located between 30° N and 30° S latitude.
3. The weather in the tropics is always hot.
4. The farther you move from the equator, the cooler it gets.
5. Parallels of latitude are used to measure changes in temperature.
6. Low latitudes are found between 30° north and south of the equator.
7. Low latitudes have high temperatures.
8. High latitudes are found between 60° and 90° north and south of the equator.
9. High latitudes have low temperatures.

REVIEW QUESTIONS (PAGE 49)
1. What is a conformal map?
    A conformal map is one that maintains the true shapes of land masses but not the sizes. Lines of longitude and latitude cross at right angles as they do on a globe.
2. How does latitude affect temperature?
    Your latitude determines whether or not you receive direct rays from the sun. At low latitudes where you receive direct rays, the temperature is hotter. At higher latitudes where you receive indirect rays, the temperature is cooler.
3. At what latitude is the tropic of Cancer? At what latitude is the tropic of Capricorn?
    The tropic of Cancer is at 23.5° N; the tropic of Capricorn is at 23.5° S.
4. If someone told you to find 112° N, what would you say?
    Parallels of latitude only go to 90° N or S. There is no 112° N.
5. Where do the direct rays of the sun end?
    Direct rays end at 23.5° N (the tropic of Cancer) and 23.5° S (the tropic of Capricorn).
6. Where will you find the tropics? What is another name for the tropics?
    The tropics are between 23.5° N and 23.5° S. They are also known as the low latitudes.
7. Where will you find the high latitudes?
    The high latitudes are between 60° and 90° north and south of the equator.
8. Where will you find the middle latitudes?
    The middle latitudes are between 30° and 60° north and south of the equator.
9. Why do the high latitudes have low temperatures?
    The high latitudes don't receive direct rays from the sun, so the temperature is lower than the areas of the earth that do receive direct rays.
10. Why do we have imaginary lines at 66.5° N and S?
    These lines mark the areas known as the Arctic and Antarctic Circles. In the areas above these lines, the sun stays above the horizon one or more days each year.

VOCABULARY
1. **tropics**: the area between 23.5° N and 23.5° S latitude.
2. **tropic of Cancer**: the 23.5° N parallel of latitude.
3. **tropic of Capricorn**: the 23.5° S parallel of latitude
4. **low latitudes:** the area between 30° N and 30° S latitude.
5. **high latitudes**: areas between 60° and 90° north and south of the equator.
6. **correlation**: a complimentary, reciprocal relationship between two or more things.
7. **Arctic Circle**: the parallel of latitude at 65.5° N.
8. **Antarctic Circle**: the parallel of latitude at 65.5° S.
9. **middle latitudes**: the areas between 30° and 60° north and south of the equator.

Lesson 10

Review Statements
1. The earth is tilted 23.5° on its axis.
2. The axis is an imaginary pole that goes through the North and South Poles.
3. The earth makes one turn, or rotation, on its axis every 24 hours.
4. One rotation equals one day.
5. The earth makes one revolution around the sun every 365 1/4 days.
6. One revolution equals one year.
7. The summer solstice on June 21st is the day when the sun's rays are as far north of the equator as they will ever be.
8. The winter solstice on December 22nd is the day when the sun's rays are as far south of the equator as they will ever be.

Review Questions (page 54)
1. What is the difference between large scale and small scale maps?

   A large scale map shows a large amount of detail over a small area and a small scale map shows a small amount of detail over a large area.
2. Where do the rays of the sun always shine most directly?

   They shine most directly in the tropics between 30° N and 30° S of the equator.
3. Explain "land of the midnight sun."

   On June 21, the summer solstice, the sun's rays are above the horizon in the Arctic for twenty-four hours in the northernmost parts. There is sunshine at midnight in these parts of the Arctic.
4. Explain why on July 4th, we can be the farthest distance away from the sun and still experience the hottest season of the year.

   During July the sun's rays are more direct because of the angle of the earth's axis. Even though we are farther away from the sun the more direct rays cause us to have hot weather.
5. Which direction does the Earth spin in its rotation?

   It spins from west to east

Vocabulary
1. **axis**: an imaginary pole that passes through the earth connecting the North and South Poles.
2. **rotation**: a complete (360°) spin on an axis.
3. **revolution**: a complete trip around a circle or orbit.
4. **leap year**: every fourth year. In a leap year, a day is added to the end of February (February 29th).
5. **conversely**: in the opposite way.
6. **ellipse**: an elongated circle, or oval.
7. **summer solstice**: June 21st. On this day, the sun's rays are as far north of the equator as they will ever be.
8. **equinox**: March 21st and September 22nd, periods of equal day and night.
9. **winter solstice**: December 22nd. On this day, the sun's rays are as far south of the equator as they will ever be.
10. **perihelion**: the point at which the earth is nearest the sun.
11. **aphelion**: the point at which the earth is farthest away from the sun.

Chapter 4 Review   Prime Time Longitude

LESSON 11

REVIEW STATEMENTS
1. Meridians of longitude stretch from the North Pole to the South Pole.
2. Meridians of longitude are not parallel.
3. Meridians of longitude divide the earth into the Western and Eastern Hemispheres.
4. Meridians of longitude are used to establish time.
5. The prime meridian is at 0° longitude and runs through Greenwich, England.
6. The International Date Line is at 180° longitude.
7. The prime meridian and the 180° meridian combine to form a great circle that divides the earth into the Eastern and Western Hemispheres.
8. Absolute location is the location according to latitude and longitude.

REVIEW QUESTIONS (PAGE 58)
1. List the five major parts of a map and define each.
   Title: tells the reader the subject of the map.
   Legend: shows colors, patterns, or symbols used on the map and what they represent.
   Grid System: the interlocking set of lines established by parallels of latitude and meridians of longitude which is used to find an exact location.
   Direction: shows the cardinal and/or intermediate directions on the map
   Scale: shows the size relationship of the items on the map using a representative fraction.
   2. Which map projection will give you the true shape of Antarctica?
   Polar projection.
3. List the Jovian planets.
   Jupiter, Saturn, Uranus, and Neptune.
4. What is a great circle route?
   A great circle route is travel between any two points along a great circle.
5. Are all meridians the same length? Are all parallels of latitude the same length?
   Yes, all meridians of longitude are the same length, as they measure from the north pole to the south pole. Parallels of latitude are not all the same length, changing to reflect the spherical shape of the earth.
6. Why does the prime meridian pass through Greenwich, England?
   Scientists decided in 1884 official time would be determined at the Royal Observatory in Greenwich, England. Since we use meridians of longitude to measure time, it only makes sense that the prime meridian pass through Greenwich, England
7. What is a global grid?
   A global grid is the grid formed on a globe by the intersecting lines of latitude and longitude.
8. What units are used on maps to give directions that are more specific than degrees?
   Minutes and seconds

VOCABULARY

1. **prime meridian**: the 0° meridian from which all longitude is measured east and west. It passes through Greenwich, England, site of the Royal observatory.
2. **longitude**: distance measured east and west of the prime meridian.
3. **meridian**: a line extending from pole to pole that measures longitude.
4. **merge**: to unite, blend or come together.
5. **circumference**: the outer boundary of a circular area.
6. **absolute location**: location according to latitude and longitude.

LESSON 12

CRITICAL THINKING ACTIVITY: WHAT TIME IS IT? (PAGE 61)

You are the president of a worldwide company. Each day of the week you call one of your divisional managers at their different locations. Here is your calling schedule:

Day	Office Location	Latitude and Longitude Location
Monday	Boise, Idaho	43° 36' 49" N, 116° 12' 09" W
Tuesday	St. Louis, Missouri	38° 38' 10" N, 90° 14' 39" W
Wednesday	Paris, France	48° 51' 00" N, 2° 20' 00" E
Thursday	Tokyo, Japan	35° 41' 00" N, 139° 44' 00" E
Friday	Quito, Equador	0° 07' 59" S, 78° 28' 59" W
Home Office	Los Angeles, California	34° 03' 44" N, 118° 13' 40" W

Listed beside each city is its latitude and longitude location. Using the location of each city and the time zone map (Fig. 4-6) determine what time would you have to call from Los Angeles to speak with your managers at 1:00 p.m. their time.

Call from Los Angeles to Boise at 12:00 p.m. (Los Angeles time.)
Call from Los Angeles to St. Louis at 11:00 a.m. (Los Angeles time.)
Call from Los Angeles to Paris at 4:00 a.m. (Los Angeles time.)
Call from Los Angeles to Tokyo at 8:00 p.m. (Los Angeles time.)
Call from Los Angeles to Quito at 10:00 a.m. (Los Angeles time.)

Why is it better to call Tokyo on Thursday instead of Friday?
If we called Tokyo on Friday from Los Angeles, it would be Saturday in Tokyo, and we probably would not find anyone working. To reach Tokyo on Friday (Tokyo time), we must call from Los Angeles on Thursday (Los Angeles time).

REVIEW STATEMENTS

1. Sun time is based directly on the sun's position.
2. Greenwich Mean Time (GMT) is the time at the Royal Observatory in Greenwich, England.
3. All standard time is based upon Greenwich Mean Time (GMT).
4. The prime meridian is at 0° longitude and runs through Greenwich, England.
5. If you move east of the prime meridian you advance in time.
6. If you move west of the prime meridian you decrease in time.
7. A.m. stands for "ante meridian" which means "before the meridian."
8. P.m. stands for "post meridian" which means "after the meridian."
9. Daylight saving time moves the time ahead one hour from April to October.

REVIEW QUESTIONS (PAGE 63)

1. Which two continents appear to be one?
   Europe and Asia.
2. What is the name of the sea near the middle of the Atlantic Ocean?
   The Sargasso Sea.
3. Which map projection is conformal?
   A Mercator projection.
4. What is a compass rose?
   A compass rose is a diagram found on a map or globe which indicates cardinal and intermediate directions.
5. If you wanted to draw a map for the purpose of telling time, how many degrees apart would you draw your meridians of longitude?
   15°
6. Will the time change at 15° E if you move from the Northern to the Southern Hemisphere?
   No
7. It is 1:00 p.m. in Miami, Florida. What time is it in Dallas, Texas?
   It is 12:00 p.m., or noon.
8. It is noon in Denver, Colorado. What time is it in Santa Fe, New Mexico?
   It is the same time, noon.
9. It is 3:00 p.m. in Los Angeles, California. What time is it in Topeka, Kansas?
   5:00 p.m.
10. Discuss how using standard time benefits us in the modern world.
    Using standard time provides a convenient way for large areas to use the same time. It helps in scheduling transportation, in doing business, in communications, etc.

VOCABULARY

1. **sun time**: a measurement of time that is directly based on the position of the sun.
2. **standard time**: a method of measuring time based on time at the prime meridian.
3. **Greenwich Mean Time (GMT)**: The mean or average time established at the meridian in Greenwich, England, and used as the basis for determining time worldwide.
4. **post meridian**: past the meridian.
5. **ante meridian**: before the meridian.
6. **daylight saving time (DST)**: moving time ahead one hour from the first Sunday in April to the last Sunday in October.

LESSON 13

CRITICAL THINKING ACTIVITY: (PAGE 66)
If you move west from L.A. to the international date line, how many hours difference are there?
> *Four hours.*

(All other answers are provided in the activity.)

HANDS-ON ACTIVITY: NOW LET'S FLY TO RIYADH, SAUDI ARABIA (PAGE 67)
Look at the globe and locate Los Angeles. The absolute location is 34.04° N 118.14° W.
Tape your string over Los Angeles. Now locate Riyadh, Saudi Arabia. The absolute location is
24.31°N 46.47°E.

1. Stretch your string *west* from Los Angeles to Riyadh. What happens when you try to pull the string tight?
   > *The string curves up the globe over the Arctic Circle.*
2. Stretch your string *east* from Los Angeles to Riyadh. What happens when you try to pull the string tight?
   > *The string curves up the globe over the Arctic Circle.*

Notice that the string automatically finds the shortest distance following the spherical shape of the earth. What do we call this shortest distance?
> *A great circle route.*

Does this help you to understand that a great circle route is the shortest distance between two places on the earth?

The actual great circle route distance between L.A. and Riyadh is 8,283 miles (13,331 km).

REVIEW STATEMENTS
1. The International Date Line is 180°.
2. When you go west of the International Date Line, the day changes to a later one. If it is Monday in Seattle, then it is Tuesday in Japan.
3. When you go east of the International Date Line, the day changes to an earlier one. If it is Tuesday in Japan, then it is Monday in Seattle.

REVIEW QUESTIONS (PAGE 67)
1. Why is a globe the most accurate representation of the earth?
   > *It is a three-dimensional object that can show the height, width, and depth of the earth accurately.*
2. What is an azimuthal projection?
   > *An azimuthal projection is a circular projection that shows one-half of the globe. Distances on an azimuthal projection accurately reflect the curved surface of the earth.*
3. What is centrifugal force?
   > *It is the force that moves objects in a curved motion away from the center of the curve.*
4. What is the meridian of longitude at the International Date Line?
   > *180°*
5. Is the International Date Line a straight line?
   > *No, it changes to meet the needs of the people that live close to it.*

VOCABULARY

1. **International Date Line:** an imaginary line at the 180° meridian of longitude that connects with the prime meridian to create a great circle.

BRAIN TEASER (PAGE 67)

Have you ever wondered why geographers always use cardinal and intermediate directions rather than up, down, right, and left? If you were standing at the North Pole how would you tell your friend in L.A. to meet you in Tokyo?

Travel west from Los Angeles across the Pacific Ocean to 35° 41' N, 139° 44' E.

Now, if you were at the South Pole would your directions be any different?

No

Think like a geographer and you will always be at the right place, time, and hemisphere.

Chapter 5 Review Journey to the Center of the Earth (The Lithosphere)

Lesson 14

Breaking down words into their parts (page 74)
Can you break down the meanings of the following words?

>**geologist** - geo = earth; logy = the study of; ist = one who
>   *A geologist is one who studies the earth.*
>**subnormal** - sub = beneath, below, under; normal = conforming to a standard
>   *Subnormal means something is below standard.*
>**disapprove** - dis = not, the opposite of; approve = to consider right, to accept
>   *Disapproval is the opposite of approving something. You do not approve, accept, or consider right.*
>**subsonic** - sub = beneath, below, under; sonic = the speed of sound
>   *Subsonic means below the speed of sound.*
>**aqueduct** - aqua = water; duct = to carry or channel
>   *An aqueduct carries or channels water.*
>**distrust** - dis = not, the opposite of; trust = to rely on
>   *Distrust is the opposite of relying on someone or something. You do not trust.*

Review Statements
1. The four sections of the earth are the inner core, outer core, mantle and crust.
2. The core is divided into the inner core and outer core.
3. The mantle is divided into the lower mantle and upper mantle.
4. The upper mantle is called the asthenosphere.
5. The crust includes the Moho and the oceanic and continental plates.
6. The crust is called the lithosphere.

Review Questions (page 75)
1. What is an ellipse?
    An ellipse is an elongated circle, or oval.
2. List the four hemispheres of the earth.
    They are the Northern, Southern, Eastern, and Western Hemispheres.
3. List the four layers of the earth.
    The four layers are inner core, outer core, mantle, and crust (or lithosphere).
4. How do we know the interior of the earth is hot? Be specific.
    We know by observing molten lava erupting from volcanoes, as well as by feeling increasing heat as we go down into a mine.
5. According to scientists, the earth's core should be made of what material? What other objects consist of this material?
    The earth's core should be made of a nickel-iron alloy. Meteorites also consist of this material.
6. How do we know there are four layers within the earth?
    We know from using sound waves in a process called remote sensing.
7. Have we drilled through the Moho?
    No.

8. Where is the earth's crust the thickest? Where is it the thinnest?

    It is thickest under mountains and glaciers, and thinnest under the shallow seas.

VOCABULARY

1. **inner core**: the innermost 750 miles of the earth.
2. **remote sensing**: gathering information without being in physical contact with the object studied (i.e., aerial photography, radar, and sonar).
3. **outer core**: the layer of the earth extending 1,410 miles beyond the inner core.
4. **mantle**: the middle layer of the earth between the core and the crust.
5. **crust**: the top layer of the earth.
6. **core**: the central layer of the earth, occupying a fifth of our planet's volume. Includes both the inner and outer cores. Extends 2,160 miles from the very center of the earth.
7. **alloyed**: mixed with one or more additional metals.
8. **deduce**: reach a conclusion by reasoning from known facts.
9. **magma**: molten material beneath the earth's crust.
10. **lava**: magma that has reached the earth's surface.
11. **asthenosphere**: the outer part of the mantle, and the origin of magma.
12. **lithosphere**: the earth's crust, the rigid layer on top of the mantle which drifts on the softer asthenosphere below.
13. **Moho**: the boundary between the lithosphere and the asthenosphere.
14. **density**: a measure of the amount of mass within a given area.
15. **prefix**: the part attached to the front of a base word.
16. **suffix**: the part attached to the end of a base word.
17. **geographer**: one who writes about or draws maps of the earth.
18. **meteorologist**: one who specializes in the study of astronomical phenomena.
19. **geologist**: one who specializes in the study of the earth and its history.

LESSON 15

REVIEW STATEMENTS

1. Sonar is used to map the ocean floor.
2. The continents are being slowly pushed apart due to the spreading of the rift along the Mid-Atlantic Ridge.
3. Oceanic crust subducts, or moves beneath, continental crust.
4. Plate tectonics is today's theory to explain the forces that destroy and rebuild the earth.

REVIEW QUESTIONS (PAGE 80)

1. What is absolute location?

    Absolute location is location according to latitude and longitude.

2. List the seven continents.

    Asia, Africa, North America, South America, Antarctica, Europe, and Australia

3. In what part of the world did natives blame the goddess Pele for earthquakes and volcanoes?

    Polynesia

4. What did the Aztecs do in an attempt to keep the gods happy?

    They built temples and burned the hearts of sacrificial captives.

5. Why were there so few deaths in the Anchorage earthquake?

    Because of the sparse population, the lack of tall buildings where people might have gathered, and the stores being closed in observance of Good Friday.

6. What was developed in WWII that helps geologists see underwater? How does it work?

Sonar. It is a form of remote sensing that sends out high-pitched sound waves like a bat uses, which bounce off everything in their path. Technicians then analyze the echoes to determine what is around them.

7. Why had scientists believed the oldest rocks on earth were on the seafloor?

Because the soil on land eventually washes into the ocean and the oldest material would have settled on the ocean floor long ago and remained there.

8. Why does oceanic crust subduct below continental crust?

Because it is heavier than continental crust.

Vocabulary

1. **Richter scale**: a scale that measures the severity of earthquakes, with each whole-number increase indicating ten times more ground movement and about thirty times more energy.
2. **epicenter**: the point on the surface of the earth lying directly above the center of an earthquake.
3. **tsunami**: giant destructive waves created by undersea earthquakes or underwater landslides.
4. **Axis**: the alliance formed by Germany, Italy, and Japan during WWII.
5. **Allies**: the alliance formed by Great Britain, France, the United States, and others during WWII.
6. **sonar**: **so**und **na**vigation **r**anging; also used by physicians to "see" an unborn baby in the mother's womb.
7. **Mid-Atlantic Ridge**: a long, continuous underwater mountain range, formed by volcanic outpourings from the asthenosphere, that lies roughly parallel to continental margins. The center is marked by a steep V.
8. **sediment**: crustal debris that has been deposited by wind, water, or ice.
9. **hypothesis**: something assumed because it seems likely to be a true explanation. Not yet a proven theory.
10. **rift**: a tear in the earth's crust.
11. **seafloor spreading**: the theory that oceanic ridges are formed by magma rising from the mantle and forcing the plates apart.
12. **ocean basin:** the portion of the seafloor extending from one side of a ridge to a continental margin.
13. **abyssal plains:** the flattest regions of the ocean seafloor, near the continental margins.
14. **plate tectonics**: the interaction of the crustal plates that produces earthquakes, volcanoes, and mountains while destroying old crust and creating new crust.
15: **subduction**: the movement of the ocean floor beneath the continental crust.
16. **convection**: the transfer of heat from one place to another by the movement of heated particles of gas or a liquid.

Lesson 16

Review Statements

1. There are three ways tectonic plates react.
2. The plates can converge or come together.
3. The plates can diverge or move away from each other.
4. The plates can strike-slip or slip past each other.
5. When continents collide they change shape and form mountains.

REVIEW QUESTIONS (PAGE 86)

1. Where are the tropics located?

    The tropics are in the area between 23.5° N and 23.5° S latitude.

2. What kind of plate interaction occurs at the San Andreas fault? What is happening there?

    Transform, or strike-slip. The little bit of continental crust we call coastal southern California lies on the Pacific plate moving northward, while the rest of California lies on the North American plate moving southward. One plate will eventually build up enough pressure to jerk away from the other, causing an earthquake.

3. Why are continents unable to subduct?

    They are too buoyant, and they are lighter than oceanic crust.

4. What happens when two oceanic plates collide? What can result from this collision?

    When two oceanic plates collide, the heavier one will subduct. A deep trench forms in the subduction zone. The result can be volcanic activity on the seafloor that may eventually form islands.

5. How were the Himalayas formed? Two continental plates collided.

    The Indian plate rammed into the Asian plate lifting up the Himalayas.

6. Where do most divergent boundaries occur?

    Most divergent boundaries occur along the outer portions of continents where the crust is the thinnest.

7. Is it possible to have continental and oceanic crust on the same plate? Why?

    Yes. This is possible because the plates are so big that both land and oceans or seas are found on many of the plates.

VOCABULARY

1. **plates**: huge rigid slabs of crust.
2. **plate tectonics:** the interaction of the crustal plates that produces earthquakes, volcanoes and mountains while destroying old crust and creating new crust.
3. **seismic activity:** movement of the earth.
4. **seismograph:** an instrument used to measure movement of the earth.
5. **subduction:** the movement of the ocean floor beneath the continental crust.
6. **buoyant**: able to rise or float in the air or on the surface of a liquid.
7. **converge**: to come together. This occurs when two plates are drawn together and collide.
8. **diverge**: to separate. This occurs when two plates move apart.
9. **transform** or **strike-slip**: when one plate moves past another in an opposite direction involving very little change.
10. **fault**: a crack in the earth's bedrock along which movement has occurred.

LESSON 17

REVIEW STATEMENTS

1. An earthquake is a movement of the earth's crust.
2. The Richter scale is the scale used by scientists to measure the intensity of an earthquake.
3. Earthquakes are not predictable at this time.
4. Most earthquakes occur at a plate boundary but may occur anywhere there is a weakness in the crust.
5. Waterlogged soil liquefies during an earthquake.

REVIEW QUESTIONS (PAGE 94)

1. In your own words, explain the mechanics of a seismograph.

    A seismograph may be lasers aligned or a simple pen balanced over a roll of paper. When the earth moves, the lasers or the pen record the movement.

2. How do geologists discover new faults?

    When an earthquake occurs along the fault.

3. What is the difference between the Richter scale and the Mercalli scale?

    The Richter scale gives an actual measurement of the movement of the earth. The Mercalli scale is based on survivors' reports of the damage caused.

4. Why can people at rest feel earthquakes that others can not feel?

    When you are standing, only your feet are in contact with the ground. When you are at rest, more of your body is in contact with the ground, such as through a chair or bed, allowing you to feel the vibrations of a small earthquake.

5. Describe the San Andreas fault.

    The San Andreas fault is a strike-slip fault where the North American and Pacific plates come together.

6. What is the difference between the focus and the epicenter of an earthquake?

    The focus is the site of the cause of the earthquake. The epicenter is the spot on the surface of the earth directly above the focus.

7. Explain why earthquakes east of the Rockies cover a much larger area than those on the West Coast.

    The bedrock in the area east of the Rockies is more solid and thus the vibrations of an earthquake travel much farther.

8. What happened to Turnagain Heights in 1964?

    A strong earthquake liquefied the soil and caused a massive slide.

9. Why did San Francisco burn to the ground after the 1906 earthquake?

    Because water lines were broken, so there was no way to fight the fires started by broken gas lines.

10. How does an earthquake cause an avalanche?

    The movement of the earth dislodges snow, rocks, and mud from steep mountainsides, causing an avalanche.

11. What causes most of the deaths in an earthquake?

    Collapsing buildings cause the most deaths in an earthquake.

VOCABULARY

1. **earthquake**: any abrupt movement of the earth.
2. **seismologist:** a person who studies the movements of the earth.
3. **Richter scale:** a logarithmic scale measuring the intensity of an earthquake.
4. **Mercalli scale:** an arbitrary ranking of earthquake destruction based on observations of survivors.
5. **focus:** the true center of an earthquake.
6. **epicenter:** the point on the surface of the earth that is directly above the focus.
7. **confluence:** a point at which streams or rivers come together.
8. **aftershocks:** small earthquakes coming after a large one.
9. **foreshocks:** small earthquakes coming before a large one.
10. **avalanche:** a rapidly descending mass, usually of snow, down a mountainside.

Chapter 6 Review   Mountain Building

Lesson 18

Review Statements
1. Orogenesis is the process of building mountains.
2. A cordillera is a mountain system that includes numerous mountain ranges.
3. There are two principle cordilleras on the earth. One creates the "Ring of Fire" in the Pacific and the other comes together at the Pamir Knot in central Asia.
4. Plates can strike-slip, or slip past each other.
5. When continents collide they change shape and form mountains.

Review Questions (page 102)
1. List the four layers of the earth.
    The inner core, outer core, mantle and crust.
2. What is magma?
    Magma is molten material beneath the earth's crust.
3. What is the difference between a mountain range and a cordillera?
    A cordillera is a system of mountains, and a mountain range is a specific group of mountains found within a cordillera.
4. Where is the deepest part of the earth's surface found?
    In the Challenger Deep portion of the Marianas Trench.
5. What is the difference between a mountain and a plateau?
    Mountains and plateaus can both be a thousand feet above the surrounding land surface. The difference between the two is that the mountain has peaks, while a plateau has a flat top.
6. Why are there so many trenches surrounding the Pacific Ocean?
    Trenches are formed where subduction takes place, and there is a great deal of subduction surrounding the Pacific Ocean.
7. Describe the Ring of Fire.
    The Ring of Fire is a series of volcanic mountains encircling the Pacific Ocean. It is formed along the subduction zone regions that encircle the Pacific Ocean.
8. What was the importance of the Cumberland Gap in the Appalachians?
    The Cumberland Gap provided a passageway through the Appalachians for Native Americans as well as for later settlers such as Daniel Boone.
9. Why will you find most of the earth's active volcanoes along continental boundaries?
    Most volcanoes form along zones of subduction, and most continental boundaries are also subduction zones.
10. How does an island arc form?
    An island arc forms when oceanic crust subducts and slides into the mantle, creating a series of undersea volcanoes, which over time eventually build up into islands.
11. What is the difference between a seamount and an island?
    A seamount is an underwater mountain that does not break the water surface. An underwater mountain whose top is above the surface of the water at all times is an island.

VOCABULARY

1. **orogenesis**: the process of building mountains.
2. **mountain**: a sharp and steep-sided surface area at least 300 meters above the surrounding land surface, with considerable bare rock surface.
3. **high relief**: having a large difference in elevation between the highest and lowest points.
4. **low relief**: having a small difference in elevation between the highest and lowest points.
5. **elevation**: height above sea level.
6. **cordillera**: the Spanish name for a mountain system.
7. **mountain system**: a series of more-or-less parallel mountain ranges.
8. **mountain range**: a series of mountain ridges closely related in direction and position.
9. **Ring of Fire**: volcanic mountains encircling the Pacific Ocean.
10. **trench**: a long, narrow depression in the seafloor, produced by bending of oceanic crust during subduction.
11. **island arc**: a volcanic island chain formed where the subducting plate melts back into the mantle.
12. **seamount**: a mountain, rising from the seafloor, that does not break the water surface.
13. **Pamir Knot**: a highland region of south central Asia, mostly in Tajikistan with extensions in northern Afghanistan, northern Kashmir, and western China, rising up to 24,590 feet (7,500 meters).
14. **gap**: a mountain pass, or opening, made by a break in the mountains.

LESSON 19

REVIEW STATEMENTS

1. Four ways mountains are formed are through collision, subduction, obduction, and hot spots.
2. The Ural Mountains divide Europe and Asia.
3. Collision is the coming together of two plates.
4. Subduction occurs when the heavier oceanic crust is forced under the lighter continental crust.
5. Obduction occurs when seafloor sediment becomes attached to the overriding continental crust during subduction.
6. A hole is burned through the lithosphere as it slowly moves across a hot spot. Lava oozes out through the opening and eventually forms mountains.

REVIEW QUESTIONS (PAGE 109)

1. What problems do cartographers face in drawing the earth?
   Cartographers must draw a three-dimensional object on a two-dimensional piece of paper. This means deciding whether to draw accurate shape, size, distance or direction.
2. In your own words explain the process of subduction.
   Subduction is the movement of the ocean floor beneath the continental crust.
3. Why does oceanic crust subduct below continental crust?
   Because oceanic crust is heavier than continental crust.
4. Which mountains form the seam uniting Europe and Asia?
   The Ural Mountains.
5. The San Andreas fault divides which two plates?
   The North American plate and the Pacific plate.

6. Explain each of the four mountain-building methods and give an example of each.
    1) *Collision is the crushing of two crustal plates with such pressure that the leading crustal edges are pushed up to create maintains. An example of this is the Himalayan Mountains.*
    2) *Subduction is when oceanic crust moves under continental crust to form mountains. An example of this is the Cascade Mountains.*
    3) *Obduction is where seafloor sediment becomes attached to the overriding continental plate during subduction. An example of this is the Olympic Range.*
    4) *Hot spots form mountains by burning a hole through the lithosphere where lava oozes out and eventually builds up into a mountain. As the plates move over the hot spot a new hole will be burned into the lithosphere and a new mountain will be created. An example of this is the Hawaiian Islands.*

7. Explain why the tallest of the Hawaiian islands are the newest ones.
    The tallest of the Hawaiian islands are the newest because they are still directly above the hot spot and still growing. The smaller ones have been worn down by erosion.

8. In your own words explain why Old Faithful erupts so faithfully.
    The magma chamber beneath Yellowstone heats the underground water at a steady rate. The period of time between eruptions is the amount of time required to heat the water to the boiling point.

9. Why did the ash from the last three eruptions in Yellowstone blow to the south?
    Because of the prevailing westerlies, the ash followed the funnel shape of the continent.

10. Why don't hot springs erupt?
    Hot springs do not erupt because the water is not confined within a vent or narrow opening and thus flows freely to the surface. No force is built up, so there is no eruption.

11. Describe a contour line and what it represents.
    A contour line connects points having the same elevation.

VOCABULARY

1. **seam or suture:** the point where two plates come together and are joined.
2. **collision:** the coming together of two plates of the earth's crust against each other with such pressure that the leading edge of the crust is pushed up to create mountains.
3. **obduction:** the process whereby seafloor sediment becomes attached to the overriding continental plate during subduction.
4. **hot spot:** a permanent place where intense heat from the mantle burns through the lithosphere.
5. **geyser:** an intermittent fountain of water and steam coming from a small hole in the earth's crust.
6. **hot spring:** a spring with water above 98°F (36.7°C).
7. **aquifer:** any geologic formation containing water.
8. **topographic map:** a map that indicates features of the earth's surface by means of contour lines.
9. **contour line:** a line on a map joining places of equal height or depth.

Lesson 20

Hands-On Activity (pages 120-121)

1. Mt. Tulik
2. Mt. Klyuchevskaya
3. Mt. Fuji
4. Mt. Pinatubo
5. Mt. Mayon
6. Krakatau
7. Mt. Erebus
8. Mt. Llullaillaco
9. Mt. Misti
10. Mt. Cotopaxi
11. Mt. Irazu
12. Mt. Santa Clara
13. Mt. Santa Maria
14. Mt. Popocatepetl
15. Mt. Paricutin
16. Mauna Loa
17. Mauna Kea
18. Mt. Lassen
19. Mt. Shasta
20. Mt. St. Helens
21. Mt. Rainier
22. Mt. Beerenberg
23. Mt. Hekla
24. Mt. Vesuvius
25. Mt. Etna
26. Volcan Karismbi
27. Mt. Kilimanjaro
28. Mt. Soufriere
29. Mt. Pelee
30. Mt. Santorini

Review Statements

1. There are three kinds of volcanoes: stratovolcanoes, cinder cones, and shield volcanoes.
2. Most volcanoes form where one plate subducts beneath another plate.
3. All continents except Australia have either active or extinct volcanoes.

Review Questions (page 122)

1. What is orogenesis?

   Orogenesis is the process of building mountains.
2. What is obduction?

   Obduction is the process whereby seafloor sediment becomes attached to the overriding continental plate during subduction.
3. What formed Old Faithful in Yellowstone National Park?

   Old Faithful was created by a hot spot.
4. Where do most volcanoes form?

   Most volcanoes form along subduction zones.
5. List the three kinds of volcanoes and explain how each is formed.

   1) A stratovolcano is formed when rocks, ash, lava, and other debris violently erupt from the earth over long periods of time.

   2) A cinder cone volcano is usually a one-time explosion of loose pyroclastic materials that are thrown into the air and fall on the sides of the mountain, thus building it up.

   3) A shield volcano is formed by thick lava flowing mostly from hot spots. Multiple eruptions build up a dome-shaped volcano.
6. If Mt. Everest is the highest point on Earth, then how can Mauna Loa and Mauna Kea be the tallest mountains?

   Mt. Everest rises 29,028 feet above sea level, but Mauna Loa and Mauna Kea extend more than 13,000 feet above sea level plus 18,000 feet below sea level, making them approximately 31,000 feet high from their bases to their peaks.

VOCABULARY

1. **volcano**: an opening in the earth's crust through which molten lava, ash and gases are forcefully thrown out from the interior of the earth.

2. **volcanic neck:** the main vent of a volcano.

3. **extinct:** no longer active.

4. **dormant:** not active, but still capable of becoming active.

5. **fumarole:** a volcanic vent emitting only gas and steam.

6. **crater:** a depression around the center of a volcano.

7. **caldera:** a large depression typically caused by the collapse of the summit area of a volcano.

8. **lava dome:** a round dome formed by pressure from lava beneath it.

9. **stratovolcano:** a volcano composed of alternating layers of ash and lava; it is geologically long-lived, may have multiple craters, and is asymmetrical in shape.

10. **cinder cone:** a geologically young hill or low volcanic mountain composed of loose pyroclastic materials that easily erode. Usually becomes extinct after one eruption.

11. **shield volcano:** a volcano composed of loose, thick, lava that oozes from the vents rather than exploding like a stratovolcano.

12. **pillow lava:** magma that cools and hardens in cold water.

13. **aa**: thick, gooey, lava with chunks of rock in it.

14. **pahoehoe**: lava that is runnier than aa, ropey and smooth in texture.

15. **viscosity:** resistance of a material to flow.

16. **lava tube:** a long, tubelike cavity formed by pahoehoe lava as it cools along the surface.

17. **basalt:** a highly fluid magma that forms lava sheets; the principal rock of the seabed.

18. **avalanche:** a rapidly descending mass, usually of snow down a mountainside.

19. **pyroclastics:** materials ejected during a volcanic eruption.

Chapter 7 Review   The Hydrosphere

Lesson 21

Review Statements
1. The atmosphere is a mixture of gases, water vapor, and solid particles extending 50 miles above the earth.
2. The atmosphere absorbs solar radiation.
3. Weather is the daily changes that occurs in specific locations in the atmosphere.
4. Climate is the average weather in a broader area over a specific period of time.
5. The adiabatic rate states that for every increase of 1,000 feet in elevation there is a 3.5°F decrease in temperature.
6. The water cycle: 1) heat from the sun evaporates water, turning it into a gas (water vapor); 2) water vapor collects around particles in the air, forming clouds; 3) clouds absorb as much water as possible and then release the water in the form of precipitation.

Review Questions (page 127)
1. List the four layers of Earth.
    The inner core, outer core, mantle and crust.
2. What is the name of the sea near the middle of the Atlantic Ocean?
    The Sargasso Sea.
3. What is the ratio of land to water in the Northern Hemisphere and the Southern Hemisphere?
    The Northern Hemisphere is 40% land and 60% water; the Southern Hemisphere is 19% land and 81% water.
4. How much of the earth's water is readily available for use?
    0.40%
5. What percentage of the United States' daily water usage is used by agriculture?
    49%
6. What is the source of energy in the water cycle?
    The sun.
7. What is a drawback to the desalination process?
    It is very expensive.
8. What percentage of the earth is covered by water?
    Approximately 71%.
9. Does the amount of water on the planet change, or is there a fixed amount?
    There is a fixed amount.
10. Describe an aquifer. Could you compare it to a swimming pool or a large storage tank?
    An aquifer is any geological formation containing water. It is not a large empty space underground like a swimming pool or a large storage tank, but rather tiny spaces in porous rocks and between rocks.
11. Discuss who you think should be able to use the water in aquifers. Should any state claim ownership? Should it be available to any state regardless of where it is located?
12. Discuss who you think should have the first right to water, cities or farms. Why?

VOCABULARY

1. **hydrosphere**: water within or surrounding the surface of the earth, including the water in the oceans and the water in the atmosphere.
2. **desalination**: the process of removing salt from sea water.
3. **aquifer**: any geologic formation containing water. It is not a large empty space underground, but rather the tiny spaces in porous rocks and between rocks.
4. **groundwater**: water held in aquifers below the surface of the earth.
4. **water table**: the upper limit of the water level when the ground is filled with water. It rises after rains and lowers as water is pumped out or there is drought.
5. **precipitation**: the movement of hail, mist, rain, sleet, or snow from the atmosphere onto the surface of the earth.
6. **permeable**: having openings or pores which allow water or gases to pass through.

LESSON 22

REVIEW STATEMENTS

1. Water is the greatest agent of change on the earth.
2. The water cycle is powered by the sun and the water is moved by gravity.
3. Seventy-five percent of all precipitation falls over the oceans.
4. There are four primary reasons why precipitations falls where it does. These are location, altitude, character of the land, and distance from the sea.

REVIEW QUESTIONS (PAGE 134)

1. What is the Mid-Atlantic Ridge?

    The Mid-Atlantic Ridge is a long, continuous underwater mountain range that lies roughly parallel to continental margins. It was formed by volcanic outpourings from the asthenosphere. The center is marked by a steep V.

2. Where are the tropics located?

    The tropics are in the area between 30° N and 30° S latitude, also known as the low latitudes.

3. What is an aquifer?

    An aquifer is any geologic formation containing water. It is not a large empty space underground like a swimming pool or a large storage tank, but rather tiny spaces in porous rocks and between rocks.

4. What does a mean annual precipitation map fail to show us?

    We don't know if the precipitation falls in a fine drizzle over a long period of time or comes in thunderstorms.

5. How does location affect precipitation?

    Location determines how much heat is received from the sun, which affects the water cycle, and this will determine how much precipitation falls. Different locations based on latitude receive different amounts of precipitation.

6. Explain why Antarctica is classified as a desert.

    Antarctica is a desert because it receives less than 10 inches of precipitation per year and has extreme temperatures. It is located in the high latitudes and receives very weak rays from the sun while being completely encircled by currents of extremely cold water, which evaporates very slowly. Although there is very little new snowfall, the snow that is there does not melt.

7. Explain the adiabatic rate. Why would this cause chapped lips in the mountains?

The adiabatic rate states that for every 1000-foot increase in altitude, the temperature drops approximately 3.5° F. Because cold air does not hold moisture and tends to be dry and thin, this would cause your lips to be chapped.

8. How can animals affect the growth of deserts?

Animals graze and crop the grasses. Their hooves tear up the roots, leaving the ground bare. Without the plants, the ground erodes much faster and will not hold the topsoil. This leads to desertification.

9. Explain why there are deserts along the western coasts of every continent.

Trade winds move the warm surface water westward leaving a void to be filled by the upwelling cold waters rising from the deep. This cold water evaporates much more slowly, and the winds blowing off the water will be cold and dry. Cold, dry winds do not hold the moisture needed to provide rain for parts of the western coasts of each continent, and these areas become deserts.

10. Where will you find areas of upwelling? Why are these areas good for fishing, but poor for farming?

Areas of upwelling will be found along the western edge of most continents. This is good for fishing because the cold upwelling waters are rich in nutrients and provide a fertile fishing ground, but the air that moves inland from the upwelling is too cold to hold enough moisture to water the land. This makes the land dry and a poor place to grow crops.

11. As a rule, why are there no deserts along the eastern coasts of continents? What is the one exception?

Along the eastern sides of the continents the wind and ocean currents are bringing warm, moist air and water from the equator. Where there is warm, moist air, there will be a wetter climate. The one exception is Africa where the Sahara winds dominate the climate in northern Africa.

12. Why is the Gobi a desert?

The Gobi is a desert because it is in the rain shadow of the Himalayas and because of the high elevation of the Tibetan Plateau. The Gobi is also too far inland to receive any moisture from the ocean.

13. Explain in your own words why 75% of all precipitation falls over the oceans.

Approximately 71% of the earth's surface is covered with water!

14. What are the four primary reasons why precipitation falls where it does?

Location, altitude, character of the land, and distance from the sea.

15. Discuss why the location of water determines the culture and economy of an area.

Man cannot live without water, nor can animals. Agriculture as well as industry require large amounts of water.

16. Discuss why different regions of the world focus on different industries based upon the location of water.

Think about how much water you use daily. Could you use water as freely as you do now if you lived in a desert? Could you grow strawberries, tomatoes, wheat, and corn without water?

Vocabulary

1. **solar energy:** energy (in the form of light or heat) coming from the sun.
2. **mean:** average, middle point between extremes, holding a middle position.
3. **desert:** a region with less than ten inches of precipitation per year and having extremes in temperature.
4. **altitude:** height above sea level.
5. **character:** that which distinguishes one object, person or thing from another.
6. **crop:** to bite or tear grasses at the roots, many times pulling up the entire plant. This leaves the soil exposed and vulnerable to erosion.
7. **trade winds:** almost constant winds blowing in the same direction; in the Northern Hemisphere they blow in a belt from northeast to southwest and in the Southern Hemisphere in a belt from southeast to northwest.
8. **upwelling:** the movement of deeper, cooler, nutrient-rich waters to the ocean surface.
9. **krill:** small, planktonic organisms that form the major food source for whales.
10. **sirocco:** a hot, dusty wind blowing from the Libyan desert of northern Africa into Italy, Malta and Sicily.
11. **prevailing westerlies:** continuous winds coming from the west.
12. **leeward:** the side or direction away from the wind.
13. **Coriolis effect:** the creation of wind patterns by the movement of the earth as it spins to the east.

Lesson 23

Review Statements

1. Most deserts are covered with desert pavement.
2. Sandy deserts are called ergs.
3. The Sahel is a dry grassland area south of the Sahara.
4. OPEC was formed to exert influence on the price of petroleum.

Review Questions (page 139)

1. What is the difference between a reg and an erg? Why do we use Arabic terms to describe these features?

    A reg is a desert without sand; an erg is a sea of sand. We use these Arabic terms because so many deserts are found in Arab countries.

2. Describe the different layers in a desert storm.

    Sand is at the bottom, and dust is at the top.

3. Discuss the importance of oases in the ability to sustain life in a desert.

    A desert is defined as a region with less than 10 inches of rain per year and extremes in temperature. Animals and people cannot live in a desert without a steady supply of water.

4. Why was the Empire of Ghana referred to as "the land of gold"?

    Because gold was used to pay for goods

5. How does the way man uses the land lead to an increase in the size of a desert?

    Hoofed animals tear up the ground, while goats and sheep crop the sparse vegetation tearing up the roots.

6. Why do deserts form in the rain shadow of mountains?

    Clouds lose their moisture as they rise to pass over mountains.

7. Explain the reasons for the existence of the Gobi Desert.

    The Gobi lies in the rain shadow of the Himalayas, in the interior of the Asian continent.

8. How does upwelling affect the location of deserts?

    Upwelling occurs in cold waters, which do not evaporate easily.

9. Why was OPEC formed, and who are the members?

    OPEC was formed to exert influence on the price of petroleum worldwide. The members are Algeria, Libya, Iraq, Iran, Kuwait, Saudi Arabia, Qatar, United Arab Emirates, Niger, Gabon, Indonesia and Venezuela.

10. Who was the first country to extend their offshore territorial claims and why?

    Venezuela wanted to lay claim to the oil in the Caribbean Sea beyond the three-mile limit of territorial rights.

VOCABULARY

1. **desert pavement:** close-fitting pebbles and stones that prevent erosion of the underlying surface.
2. **reg:** an Arabic term for "desert pavement".
3. **erg:** a sea of sand.
4. **oasis:** a point where the water table rises to the surface resulting in significant growth of vegetation.
5. **Sahel:** dry grasslands south of the Sahara.
6. **drought:** a prolonged period of dry weather; lack of rain.
7. **OPEC:** Organization of Petroleum Exporting Countries.
8. **thermal buffer:** thermal refers to heat and buffer is a zone of transition between different zones.

LESSON 24

REVIEW STATEMENTS

1. The beginning of a river is called the headwaters.
2. The ending of a river is called the mouth.
3. A continental divide is the point on a continent where the waters divide and flow into separate bodies of water.
4. The use of pollutants increases as the world population increases.

REVIEW QUESTIONS (PAGE 145)

1. In which Hemisphere, Northern or Southern, is there more water than land?

    There is more water than land in both the Northern and the Southern Hemispheres.

2. What is an upwelling?

    An upwelling is the movement of deeper, cooler, nutrient-rich waters to the surface of the ocean.

3. Where is the deepest part of the earth's surface found?

    In the Challenger Deep portion of the Marianas Trench

4. What is the difference between the headwaters and the mouth of a river?

    The headwaters is the beginning of a river, and the mouth is the end of a river.

5. Why do most rivers in the central region of the United States flow into the Mississippi River?

    The rivers flow downhill and follow the path of least resistance. The central region of the country gently slopes downhill from the continental divide in the Rockies to the east. Rivers flowing from the Appalachians flow to the west to the lowest point in the Mississippi River Valley. Rivers, therefore, will follow the slope of the land and eventually empty into the Mississippi River which then carries the water to the Gulf of Mexico.

6. Through which states does the continental divide pass?

    The continental divide passes through New Mexico, Colorado, Wyoming, Idaho and Montana.

7. List one positive and one negative result of having soil mixed into fresh water.

    Some negative results of having soil in fresh water are: it is bad to drink; it is not good to wash clothes in; and it will damage machines. Some positive effects are: the soil is deposited at the mouth of the river to renew the land and make it more fertile; and the soil deposited creates new land to use for farming or settlement.

8. Why are the Appalachian Mountains not considered a continental divide?

    The water that flows down both sides of the Appalachian Mountains eventually ends up in the same body of water, the Atlantic Ocean.

9. Does the amount of water on the planet change, or is there a fixed amount?

    There is a fixed amount

10. In your own words discuss the causes of the Dust Bowl. Do you think it can happen again?

    The Dust Bowl was caused by poor farming practices that removed the natural ground cover. Yes, it can happen again.

Vocabulary

1. **headwaters**: the beginning of a river.
2. **mouth**: the end of a river where it empties into a larger body of water.
3. **continental divide**: the point at which rivers flow in opposite directions and empty into different bodies of water.
4. **intermontane basin:** a lowland between mountains.
5. **silt**: very fine soil that is moved either by wind or water.
6. **alluvium:** soil that is carried or moved by water.
7. **alluvial deposition:** a region of soil deposited by a river.
8. **effluents:** the waste liquid flowing out of a waste-treatment plant.

Lesson 25

Review Statements

1. A summer monsoon brings rainfall while a winter monsoon is very dry.
2. The United States has the highest per-person water use in the world.
3. Industrialized nations use more water than non-industrialized nations.
4. In many areas of the world the availability or lack of water can cause great tension.

Review Questions (page 148)

1. Explain why there are deserts along the western coasts of every continent except Europe.

    Trade winds move the warm surface water westward, leaving a void to be filled by upwelling cold waters rising from the deep. This cold water evaporates much more slowly and the winds blowing off this water will be cold and dry. Cold, dry winds do not hold the moisture needed to provide rain for the western coasts of each continent, and these areas become deserts.

2. List the smaller bodies of water that are considered part of the Indian Ocean.

    The Red Sea and the Persian Gulf.

3. How do the farmers in Southern Italy compensate for their lack of water?

    The farmers rely upon crops requiring little or no water such as olives, cork, and grapes.

4. Which continent uses the most water for agriculture? Why do you think this is true?

Asia uses the most water for agriculture because it has the largest population.

5. What kind of irrigation can save over 70% of the water that is wasted by traditional sprinkling systems?

Root sprinklers.

6. Discuss some of the options countries might have to solve their water problems. How would you seek to solve the problems of water shortages?

Possible answers might include desalination, negotiating treaties, developing drought-resistant crops, fighting a war over water, and buying water.

VOCABULARY

1. **monsoon**: a seasonal wind in southern Asia and the Indian Ocean region that blows from the ocean onto the land in the summer and down from the mountains during winter. The summer monsoons bring rainfall while the winter monsoons are very dry.

LESSON 26

REVIEW STATEMENTS

1. Water is the least expensive means of transportation for commerce.
2. The St. Lawrence Seaway opened the continental interior to world trade.
3. The Mississippi is one of the most controlled rivers in the world.

REVIEW QUESTIONS (PAGE 157)

1. In your own words, discuss the importance of the physical geography and relative location of the St. Lawrence Seaway.

The St. Lawrence Seaway forms a link between the Great Lakes and the Atlantic Ocean; it creates a waterway between the agricultural interior and the industrial northeast of the United States.

2. What industries were created by the Moses Power Dam on the International Rapids part of the Seaway?

Two aluminum plants and an automobile factory were built.

3. Why is the acronym HOMES inaccurate for the purposes of a geographer?

It does not name the lakes in order of their correct relative location.

4. List the Great Lakes in order according to size.

Superior, Huron, Michigan, Erie and Ontario.

5. What determined the course of the Ohio River?

Glaciers.

6. Why does the Ohio River carry more water than the Missouri?

The Ohio River drains a region of more rainfall than the Missouri.

7. Discuss the political importance of the Red and Rio Grande Rivers.

Both rivers are political boundaries. The Red River is between two U.S. states, and the Rio Grande is between the United States and Mexico.

8. Why does the Colorado River no longer flow into the Gulf of California?

So much water is diverted from the river for agriculture and cities that there is not enough water left to reach the Gulf.

9. What two rivers are used to irrigate the valley lying between the coastal mountains of California and the Sierra Nevadas.

The Sacramento River and The San Joaquin River.

10. List at least three facts as you discuss the importance of the Yukon River.

The Yukon is navigable for the entire length of its course in Alaska. It is the third longest riverway in North America. It can be used to get to Dawson and Whitehorse, Yukon Territory, Canada.

11. Why is the Mackenzie River not as important as the Mississippi River?

The Mackenzie River freezes in winter, has little industry along its course, and is located too far north.

12. In your own words discuss why the U.S.-Mexico border is so heavily guarded.

The U.S.-Mexico border is heavily guarded because of illegal immigration and illegal drug trafficking.

VOCABULARY

1. **waterway:** a navigable body of water, such as a river, channel or canal.
2. **dredge:** to remove mud from a harbor or river.
3. **basin:** an area of low relief or depression caused by erosion.
4. **levee:** a raised bank of alluvial soil flanking a river. Artificial levees have been built along many rivers to control flooding.
5. **flood plain:** relatively flat land stretching from either side of a river until it reaches a higher elevation that stops the flow of water.
6. **alluvial soil:** soil that is carried suspended in water.
7. **silt:** fine grains of soil most often deposited by rivers.
8. **delta:** a low-lying area located at the mouth of a river formed by deposits of alluvial soil.
9. **brackish:** slightly saline.

LESSON 27

REVIEW STATEMENTS

1. The Panama Canal shortened the distance between the Atlantic and Pacific Oceans by 8,000 miles.
2. The Amazon is so large it is referred to as the River Ocean due to its huge size.
3. Lake Maracaibo in Venezuela is an important waterway for both petroleum and agricultural products.

REVIEW QUESTIONS (PAGE 161)

1. What is the importance of the relative location of the Panama Canal?

The Panama Canal connects the Atlantic and Pacific Oceans. Since it lies in the tropics it is never frozen.

2. Why is it not as important as it was 30 years ago?

The canal is too small for today's supertankers.

3. What is a "mule" in reference to the Panama Canal?

A Panama Canal "mule" is a small locomotive used to pull ships through the canal.

4. What is the difference between tides on the Pacific side and the Atlantic side of the canal?

Tides on the Pacific side rise and fall about 12.5 feet compared to only about 2 feet on the Atlantic side.

5. Who is the most frequent user of the Panama Canal?

Ships carrying American goods are the most frequent users. Japan and Canada are also frequent users.

6. Explain how the island of Marajo was formed.
   Marajo was formed by alluvial deposition with silt carried by the Amazon River.
7. What is a tidal bore?
   A tidal bore is a high tide that flows upriver at speeds in excess of 40 mph.
8. In your own words, explain what you think would interrupt navigation on a river.
   Navigation can be interrupted by freezing, rapids, waterfalls, and shallows.
9. Why do all ships sail?
   Because the word "sail" is simply a nautical term for the movement of a ship.
10. What is the largest lake in South America?
    Lake Maracaibo.

VOCABULARY

1. **isthmus:** a narrow strip of land connecting two larger land masses.
2. **lock:** a section of a waterway, closed off with gates, in which vessels are raised or lowered by adding or removing water.
3. **cut:** an engineering term for an artificially created channel or passageway.
4. **discharge:** a quantity of water measured at a specific point along a river.
5. **alluvial deposition:** a region of soil deposited by a river.
6. **tidal bore:** a high tide that rises at the mouth of a river during new and full moons, rushing upriver at speeds in excess of 40 mph.
7. **estuary:** a mouth of a river that is affected by sea tides.
8. **landlocked:** entirely surrounded by land.

LESSON 28

REVIEW STATEMENTS

1. The Nile is the longest river in the world.
2. Almost 95% of Egyptians live within 12 miles of the Nile.
3. The Nile delta is subsiding due to lack of alluvial deposition to rebuild the land.
4. All of the important waterways of Africa are interrupted by rapids or cataracts.

REVIEW QUESTIONS (PAGE 166)

1. Name the most important dam on the Nile River and discuss the problems it has created.
   The Aswan High Dam. It prevents renewal of the soil downriver, and use of fertilizers has led to increased salinity and erosion of the land.
2. What role did the Congo River play in the colonization of Africa?
   The Congo was the waterway for movement of foreigners into the interior of Africa.
3. Why can't livestock be raised on the lower course of the Niger River?
   Because of the presence of the tsetse fly, which carries a disease that is often fatal to livestock.
4. What has happened to the fish in the Niger River?
   Drought, diversion of water for irrigation, overfishing, and dams have drastically reduced the number of fish in the river.
5. What did Iraq do that led to ten years of war with Iran?
   Iraq laid claim to both sides of the Shatt-al-Arab.
6. Explain why Bangladesh is one of the poorest countries in the world.
   Because of its low elevation and subsequent annual flooding.

7. Make two comparisons between the Yellow and the Mississippi Rivers.
   Both rivers flood and carry large amounts of silt. They both pass through agricultural areas and have tremendous navigable lengths.
8. In your own words explain why you think there are no bridges crossing the Amazon River.
   The Amazon is too remote and too wide.

VOCABULARY
1. **cataract:** a large or high waterfall
2. **Hindu:** a religion and culture native to India
3. **distributary:** a small channel that has broken off from a larger channel of a river.
4. **loess:** fine-grained topsoil carried by wind or water.
5. **deforestation:** the indiscriminate cutting or overharvesting of trees for lumber or to clear the land for agriculture or development.

CRITICAL THINKING ACTIVITY (PAGE 167)
Part One:
How can three rivers that are so close together at one point take such completely different paths and reach the ocean at points more than 1,000 miles apart?
   These three rivers flow into separate bodies of water as they follow the path of least resistance and flow from the highest point to the lowest point.

Part Two:
1. Which river lies farthest to the east? Where is its mouth?
   The Nile is the farthest east. Its mouth is at the Mediterranean Sea.
2. Which river lies farthest to the south? Where is its mouth?
   The Zambezi is the farthest south. Its mouth is at the Indian Ocean.
3. Which river lies farthest to the west? Where is its mouth?
   The Niger is the farthest west. Its mouth is at the Atlantic.
4. Do all these rivers have hydroelectric dams?
   Yes.
5. Do all these rivers have cataracts that interrupt navigation?
   Yes.
6. Do they all form deltas at their mouths?
   Yes.

LESSON 29

REVIEW STATEMENTS
1. Paris can trace its roots to pre-Roman times.
2. The Rhone River flows to the south and empties into the Mediterranean.
3. The Rhine River is Europe's most important river.
4. The Elbe River is of historic significance as the dividing line between Soviet occupation of Germany and that of the Allied nations.
5. The Danube flows to the east away from the heavily industrialized regions of Europe.

REVIEW QUESTIONS (PAGE 172)

1. Look at the map of Europe, Fig. 7-73 and name the mountain ranges in Europe.

   The Pyrenees, Alps, Appennines, Carpathians, Caucasus and Urals.

2. Discuss the importance of the Seine River to Paris, France.

   The Seine supplies most of the city's water requirement. It is a major transportation artery, and its water is important for irrigation and to cool industrial plants.

3. Where is the mouth of the Seine?

   At the English Channel.

4. In your own words explain how the Rhone could be too turbulent for navigation, yet the major roads follow its path. Think like a geographer, now!

   The Rhone River has impassable rapids, while the roads can be smoothed out, graded and paved along the route carved out by the river.

5. What type of industries line the banks of the Rhine?

   Many types of industries line the banks of the Rhine, including chemical, food product, textile, metal goods, vehicle, rubber, oil refining, and shipbuilding.

6. Where is the mouth of the Rhine?

   At Rotterdam, Netherlands at the North Sea.

7. What importance does the Rhine have to Basel, Switzerland?

   The Rhine provides a waterway to the North Sea.

8. How did sailors explain the numerous accidents between Mainz and Koblenz on the Rhine?

   They attributed the accidents to the mesmerizing voices of the sirens that lured the sailors onto the rocks.

9. What role did the Elbe play toward the end of World War II?

   The Elbe was the dividing line between Soviet occupation and that of the Allies.

10. In your own words explain how the major rivers of Europe are all connected.

    The major rivers of Europe are connected by canals.

11. Why isn't the Danube as important as the Rhine?

    The Danube flows away from the industrialized regions of Europe, while the Rhine flows through these regions.

12. Who built the Iron Gate hydroelectric dam?

    Romania and Yugoslavia built the Iron Gate dam.

13. Why did Hungary back out on the construction of a dam across the Danube?

    Hungary felt that the dam would alter the river's flow and damage surrounding lands.

14. What did the International Court of Justice rule in this dispute?

    The court ruled that both countries had violated the original agreement, needed to compensate each other, and that they should continue negotiations.

15. What is an estuary and how does it affect navigation?

    An estuary is the mouth of a river that is affected by tides. Boats may not be able to dock upriver at low tide, while downriver docks are never high and dry.

VOCABULARY

1. **siren:** in Greek and Roman mythology, a sea nymph whose sweet singing lured mariners to their deaths on rocky coasts.
2. **draft:** the depth of water that a ship needs in order to float.
3. **Tower of London:** a fortress of several buildings in London historically used as both a palace and a prison.

Lesson 30

Review Statements

1. Australia is mostly desert due to its relative location.
2. The Great Dividing Range to the east prevents rain from moving into the interior of the continent.
3. An area of upwelling on the west coast brings only cold ocean currents.
4. The Snowy Mountain Scheme uses a series of dams, aqueducts and tunnels to provide a steady flow of water.

Review Questions (page 173)

1. Name the three major rivers of Australia.
    The Darling, Lachlan, and Murray.
2. Why is the Darling not dry during the summer?
    Because it receives rain from the highlands.
3. How is snow water moved from one place to another?
    The water is moved through a system of dams, aqueducts and tunnels.

Lesson 31

Review statements

1. The relative location of Pittsburg led to its rise as a supply center for settlers moving west and as an industrial center for iron production.
2. Transportation by water is much cheaper than by land.
3. Chicago eventually replaced Pittsburg as the most important steel center.
4. Today many industries have moved to the Sun Belt because of cheaper labor, lower taxes and more affordable housing.

Review Questions (page 176)

1. In your own words discuss the reasons for the prominence of Pittsburgh during the rush to settle the Great Plains region of North America.
    Pittsburg's relative location placed it at the "Forks of the Ohio", the beginning of the route into the continental interior. Iron products were available there, and banks and suppliers followed the market and moved to Pittsburgh.
2. Why did coke replace charcoal as the choice of fuel in the smelting of iron ore?
    Coke can reach the higher temperatures required in the smelting process for steel.
3. Prior to 1855, what prevented navigation between Lake Superior and Lake Huron?
    Rapids prevented navigation between the two lakes.
4. What effect did the earliest smoke-stack industries have on surrounding towns and forests?
    The emissions from the industrial plants killed the forests and covered the towns in a layer of greasy black soot.
5. Give three reasons why this has changed.
    Technology has improved, and there are laws regulating emissions. Also the coal tar that used to be released into the air is now used in the production of many items, including sulfa drugs, antihistamines, Vitamin A, aspirin, Novocaine, and synthetic rubber.
6. Why do you suppose the earliest industrial regions are called the Rust Belt?
    Because the industries have moved out of the region, leaving their buildings and equipment to rust and decay.

7. Why are industries moving to the Sun Belt?

Because in the Sun Belt land is cheaper, labor is less expensive, taxes are lower and housing is more affordable.

8. Where would you prefer to live and work?
9. Do you think that in time the Sun Belt will also become a Rust Belt?

VOCABULARY

1. **smelt:** to melt ores in order to remove impurities.
2. **coke:** coal from which most of the gases have been removed by heating. It burns with intense heat and little smoke.
3. **Rust Belt:** the states of the Midwest and Northeast where there has been a decrease in production of such items as steel and automobiles.
4. **Sun Belt:** the states of the South and Southwest with a warm, sunny climate.

LESSON 32

REVIEW STATEMENTS

1. Poor farming practices during the early settlement of our country led to devastating erosion.
2. The Great Depression increased the ranks of the unemployed to 13 million.
3. The Dust Bowl forced farmers into bankruptcy and off of their farms.
4. New farming practices were developed by the TVA.
5. WWII and the Korean War affected the development of the TVA through demands for war materials.

REVIEW QUESTIONS (PAGE 184)

1. Explain how erosion can drown the mouth of a river.

The eroded soil is deposited at the river's mouth, raising the ground level of that area.

2. What were the major goals of the TVA? Why was it important to meet these goals?

The major goals of the TVA were to conserve the remaining natural resources of the region, provide electricity, and raise region's productivity. This was important because of the extreme poverty and ruined farmland in the region.

3. Discuss the potential and navigational problems of the Tennessee River.

The river had great potential for hydroelectricity and to provide a connection with the Mississippi, but was unnavigable due to a 37-mile stretch of rapids.

4. In 1914, why was it important for us to have an alternate source of nitrates?

German ships were sinking supply boats coming from Chile, and we needed nitrates to build bombs.

5. Discuss life in this region during the Great Depression. Give specific examples of agriculture, health, education and family.

Annual per capita income in the Tennessee Valley was only $168, the size of families was increasing, and the people were generally uneducated and unskilled. Hunger was common, malaria affected about 30% of the people in the area, and deforestation and erosion were making the land unusable.

6. Give specific examples of agricultural solutions developed by the TVA.

The TVA developed new fertilizers, educated farmers about terracing, rotation of crops, contour plowing, strip cropping, and soil surveys, and it provided seedlings to replant forests.

7. What was the new Deal and how did it affect this region?
    The New Deal was a series of laws and agencies created in an attempt to stimulate the economy, create jobs, and pull the nation out of the Great Depression.
8. How did the TVA compete with private enterprise? Do you think this is good or bad? How did the TVA affect the price of electricity within the region?
    The TVA competed in selling electricity. It affected the price of electricity by selling it at a lower price than private enterprise could.
9. What does the presence of limestone tell us about a region?
    The presence of limestone in a region tells us that the region was once covered by a large body of water.
10. Discuss five things you learned about zinc.
    Zinc is used as a dietary supplement. It is used in insulin, batteries and cosmetics, and it prevents rust.
11. Discuss five things you learned about manganese.
    Lack of manganese disrupts growth and results in central-nervous-system disorders. Steel is hardened with manganese, and manganese is used in stainless steel, disinfectants, deodorizers and saccharin.
12. How did WWII affect the TVA and how did they address the new and different demands?
    WWII increased demand for energy to produce aluminum for airplanes. The TVA began supplying massive amounts of energy, did research into atomic bombs, and with the U.S.G.S. developed new mapping techniques based on aerial photography.
13. Why was industry attracted to this region? Give specific examples.
    There was a good transportation system, it was free from flooding, and the cost of electricity was low.
14. How did the cost of coal affect the capabilities of the TVA?
    As the cost of coal increased, it cut into profitability, so the TVA resorted to nuclear energy, but new safety standards forced the end of nuclear plant construction.
15. What are some of the concerns stalling the growth of nuclear energy?
    How to dispose of the spent rods.

VOCABULARY

1. **slash-and-burn agriculture:** the practice of clearing fields for agriculture by cutting down and burning all vegetation.
2. **Tennessee Valley Authority (TVA):** a federal corporation organized in 1933 to provide cheap electric power, flood control and irrigation by building dams and reservoirs along the Tennessee River.
3. **legumes:** any of a large family of plants that bear nodules on the roots containing nitrogen-fixing bacteria.
4. **New Deal:** a series of laws passed and agencies created in an attempt to stimulate the economy, create jobs and pull the nation out of the depression.
5. **limestone:** hard rock formed by the deposition of dead organisms and mainly consisting of calcium carbonate.
6. **stalactite:** a mass of calcite suspended from the roof of a limestone cavern.
7. **stalagmite:** an accumulation of calcite that has grown up from the floor of a limestone cavern.
8. **slag:** impure mineral waste removed in the ore-making process.
9. **reclaim:** to restore to usefulness.

10. **gasohol:** a fuel made of ethyl alcohol and unleaded gasoline. The alcohol is made from sugars and starches found in plants, mostly corn.

LESSON 33

REVIEW STATEMENTS

1. A current is a river flowing within a larger body of water.
2. Currents above the equator flow clockwise.
3. Currents below the equator flow counterclockwise.
4. The Humboldt, or Peru Current, is the strongest of the world's cold ocean currents.
5. The Gulf Stream is a warm ocean current flowing northward from the equator along the coast of North America, before turning eastward towards Europe, and becoming the North Atlantic Drift.

REVIEW QUESTIONS (PAGE 191)

1. What is a desert?

    A desert is a region with less than ten inches of precipitation per year and extremes in temperature.

2. What is the source of energy in the water cycle?

    The sun.

3. Why is the Sargasso Sea called a watery desert?

    Because of its high temperatures.

4. Which direction do ocean currents flow above and below the equator? Explain this effect in your own words, please.

    Ocean currents above the equator flow clockwise, and currents below the equator flow counterclockwise. This is called the Coriolis effect.

5. Why is the Humboldt Current cold?

    Because the water flows north from Antarctica.

6. Why is the Atacama Desert the driest place on earth? Be sure to take into account all the factors such as elevation, absolute location, etc.

    The Atacama is dry because there is an upwelling of cold water on the western coast of South America. This cold water evaporates much more slowly and the winds blowing off the water are cold and dry. The cold, dry winds do not hold the moisture needed to provide rain for parts of the Atacama area, therefore creating a desert environment.

7. Why do the low latitudes have the highest evaporation rate? Does this answer also explain the high precipitation rate?

    The low latitudes have the highest evaporation rate due to the direct rays from the sun making it hot year-round. The higher precipitation rate is a result of the higher amount of evaporation. There will be more water entering the water cycle, condensing to form clouds, and then falling as precipitation.

8. How would you explain upwelling?

    As trade winds move surface waters away, cold waters rise to take their place at the surface.

9. Why does coral grow on the east side of continents?

    Because of the warm waters flowing from the equator.

10. What effect would a river have on coral?
    Fresh water kills coral.

VOCABULARY

1. **current**: a river flowing within a larger body of water.
2. **upwelling**: the movement of deeper, cooler, nutrient-rich water to the ocean surface.
3. **coral**: stony skeletal deposits produced by polyps.
4. **Humboldt (Peru) current**: a cold ocean current flowing northward from Antarctica along the western coast of South America. Creates an area of upwelling that is one of the most important fishing areas in the world.
5. **disruptive**: interrupting or interfering with something.
6. **Gulf Stream**: a warm ocean current flowing northward along the eastern coast of North America before turning toward Europe and becoming the North Atlantic Drift.
7. **blight**: any disease that destroys plants.

LESSON 34

REVIEW STATEMENTS

1. A glacier is a large mass of land ice that is or has been in motion.
2. There are two general categories of glaciers: continental and alpine.
3. Continental glaciers form at high latitudes and cover huge areas of land.
4. Alpine glaciers form in mountains at high elevations and cover smaller areas of land.
5. Of all fresh water on the earth, 1.64% is in ice caps and glaciers.
6. Glaciers change the face of the land they travel across.

REVIEW QUESTIONS (PAGE 199)

1. What are the four primary reasons why precipitation falls where it does?
    Location, altitude, character of the land, and distance from the sea determine why precipitation falls where it does.
2. What are headwaters?
    Headwaters are the beginning of a river.
3. What must happen in order for glaciers to develop?
    In order for a glacier to develop, there must be more precipitation than evaporation. In other words, there must be more snowfall than evaporation.
4. List the two general categories of glaciers and explain their differences.
    The two categories of glaciers are continental glaciers and alpine glaciers. Continental glaciers form at high latitudes and cover huge areas of land. Alpine glaciers form in mountains at high elevations and cover smaller areas of land.
5. Describe two landforms that have been sculpted by a glacier.
    A hanging valley is a glacial tributary valley that is not as deeply eroded as the main glacial valley and thus remains higher when the glacier retreats. A cirque is a large mountain hollow created by a glacier and may be considered the headwaters of a glacier.
6. What can be considered the headwaters of a glacier?
    A cirque.
7. Why are glaciers measured in cubic measurements?
    Because they have three dimensions: height, width and depth.
8. Discuss how glaciers are similar to rivers. How are they different?

Glaciers are like rivers in that they seek the path of least resistance and they carry soil gathered along their path. They are different because glaciers can carry boulders bigger than houses, carve out great amounts of land such as the Great Lakes, depress the land hundreds of feet with their weight, and carry enough soil and rock to create landforms such as Long Island when they reach their farthest point.

Vocabulary

1. **glacier**: a large mass of land ice that is or has been in motion.
2. **continental glacier**: a glacier formed at high latitudes that covers a large area of land.
3. **alpine glacier**: a relatively small glacier formed at high elevations in the mountains.
4. **terminal moraine**: the final deposit of glacial debris marking the farthest advance of a glacier.
5. **calving**: the process whereby large pieces of ice break off when a glacier enters water.
6. **glacial scouring**: scraping action due to the weight of glaciers, leaving bare bedrock.
7. **isostasy**: the ability of the planet to seek a state of equilibrium, to equalize or balance itself.
8. **alluvial fan**: a fan-shaped stream deposit extending out from the bases of mountain ranges. Most commonly found in arid and semi-arid regions.
9. **cirque**: a large mountain hollow created by a glacier. May be considered the headwaters of a glacier.
10. **hanging valley**: a glacial tributary valley that is not as deeply eroded as the main glacial valley and thus remains higher when the glacier retreats.
11. **crevasse**: a deep crack in a glacier due to movement.
12. **plastic**: having the ability to change shape without breaking.
13. **fiord:** a long, narrow arm of the sea which formed as the result of the drowning of a glaciated valley.

Chapter 8 Review   *The Atmosphere*

LESSON 35

REVIEW STATEMENTS
1. The atmosphere is a fragile envelope of air surrounding the earth.
2. The atmosphere is a mixture of gases, water vapor, and solid particles that reaches 50 miles high.
3. The atmosphere absorbs solar radiation.
4. Climate is the average weather over an extended period of time.
5. Weather is the daily changes in climate, such as a rainy day.
6. Hot air rises and has low pressure; cold air sinks and has high pressure.

REVIEW QUESTIONS (PAGE 209)
1. In your own words explain what life would be like if air were visible.
2. What is the role of gravity in the atmosphere?
    Gravity is the force that pulls the atmosphere down to the surface of the earth.
3. Why is there almost no erosion on the moon?
    Because the moon does not have an atmosphere.
4. What would Earth be like if it didn't have an atmosphere?
    It would be like the moon, with no life.
5. Explain the symbiotic relationship between plants and people.
    Plants inhale carbon dioxide and exhale oxygen; people inhale oxygen and exhale carbon dioxide.
6. Why does your skin become dry during winter?
    Because cold air does not hold moisture.
7. Why is there a permanent low at the equator? *Beca*
    the direct rays of the sun continually evaporate the water and maintain high temperatures.
8. What happens when a front forms?
    Change occurs when a front forms.
9. What kind of weather can you expect from a high-pressure air mass? A low-pressure mass?
    A high-pressure air mass will bring relatively cooler weather, because cooler air has higher pressure. High pressure usually means clear skies and stable weather. A low-pressure air mass will bring relatively warmer temperatures. Low pressure means unstable air, perhaps bringing clouds and rain.
10. Discuss the effect of elevation on air pressure. How and why does it change?
    The adiabatic rate tells us that for every 1,000-foot increase in elevation, there will be a 3.5° F decrease in temperature. As the temperature drops, the air cools and expands, and the air pressure decreases.
11. Where do most tornadoes occur? Why?
    Most tornadoes occur in the plains region of North America because there are favorable conditions there for meeting of weather fronts.
12. What is the difference between a tornado watch and a tornado warning?
    A tornado watch means conditions are favorable for a tornado to form; a tornado warning means a tornado has been spotted.

13. Compare flowing water to flowing air. Include both warm and cold air as well as warm and cold water in your discussion.

> *Cold air sinks and cold water sinks. Warm air rises and warm water rises.*

14. Why is it so important to have oxygen masks on airplanes?

> *At the altitudes commercial airplanes fly, the air is too cold and there is not enough oxygen to support life.*

15. Explain why Seattle has so few storms and Oklahoma so many.

> *Seattle lies on the windward side of the Cascades in a maritime climate where fronts do not form. Oklahoma lies in the plains region of North America where fronts often form.*

VOCABULARY

1. **sphere**: a place or environment within which a person or thing exists.
2. **atmosphere**: a fragile envelope of air surrounding the earth.
3. **solar radiation**: the heat coming from the sun.
4. **symbiosis**: the living together of two unlike organisms for the benefit of each other.
5. **climate**: the average weather over an extended period of time.
6. **weather**: the daily changes in climate, such as a rainy day.
7. **relative humidity**: the amount of water the air can hold without dropping it in the form of precipitation.
8. **air pressure**: the force the air exerts on its surroundings due to its weight.
9. **adiabatic rate**: increase in elevation = temperature decrease with *no loss* of energy. Decrease in elevation = increase in temperature with *no gain* in energy.
10. **acclimated**: having become accustomed to a new climate.
11. **front**: area where highs and lows meet, often bringing severe weather.
12. **tornado:** rapidly rotating winds blowing around a small area of intense low pressure.

LESSON 36

REVIEW STATEMENTS

1. The Coriolis effect is created by the earth spinning to the east, creating wind patterns by its movement.
2. The direction of the wind is determined by place on the planet.
3. The doldrums is an area of calm winds found along the equator.
4. Trade winds are fairly constant winds blowing toward the equator from high-pressure zones.

REVIEW QUESTIONS (PAGE 212)

1. Why did Christopher Columbus reach San Salvador rather than New York?

> *Because the trade winds pushed him to the south rather than to the north.*

2. Why do you think the "blues" are also called the doldrums?

> *Because ships were becalmed in the area called the doldrums, stranded and running out of water and food while waiting for the winds to rise.*

3. List two thing that create wind.

> *The Coriolis effect and heat both create wind.*

4. What role do the southeast trade winds have in maintaining the Amazon Rain Forest?

> *As rain-swollen clouds rise on the continent of South America, they are constantly pushed back into the interior of the Amazon basin by these winds. There they drop their moisture once again in the rain forest.*

5. What determines wind direction?

   The place on the planet.

6. Describe the influence the Coriolis effect has on winds in the Northern and Southern Hemispheres.

   The rotation of the earth, from the west to the east, causes the winds to rotate in a clockwise pattern in the Northern Hemisphere and in a counterclockwise pattern in the Southern Hemisphere.

7. In your own words try to explain what the Ancient Mariner was experiencing.

   The Ancient Mariner was on a sailing ship becalmed in the ocean. There was no wind for many days so they could not sail, and they ran out of fresh water. They were surrounded by an ocean, but had no water to drink!

VOCABULARY

1. **Coriolis effect**: when the earth spins to the east, creating wind patterns by its movement.
2. **vortex**: a mass of swirling fluid.
3. **doldrums**: an area of calm; also referred to as the "blues".
4. **becalmed**: unable to sail due to lack of wind, motionless.
5. **horse latitudes**: the areas between 30° and 35° N and S; the calmest zones on earth.
6. **trade winds**: almost constant winds blowing in the same direction; in the Northern Hemisphere they blow in a belt from northeast to southwest, and in the Southern Hemisphere from southeast to northwest.

LESSON 37

REVIEW STATEMENTS

1. The primary way air is warmed is by contact with a warm surface.
2. The presence or absence of heat is the mechanism behind this regional wind movement.
3. Low pressure rises, and high pressure sinks.
4. A monsoon is a seasonal wind in southern Asia and the Indian Ocean region.
5. A monsoon blows from the ocean onto the land in the summer and down from the mountains during winter.

REVIEW QUESTIONS (PAGE 215)

1. Where are the high latitudes located?

   The high latitudes are the areas between 60° and 90° north and south of the equator.

2. What is the lithosphere?

   The lithosphere is the earth's crust, the rigid top of the mantle that drifts on the softer asthenosphere below.

3. How much more energy does it take to change water temperature than land temperature?

   It takes five times as much energy to change water temperature as it does to change land temperature.

4. What is the mechanism of movement for regional wind?

   The presence or absence of heat is the mechanism behind this movement.

5. Why is a valley floor colder than the sides of a mountain?

   During the day, the side of the mountain or valley receiving the most sunlight will heat up. The rising low-pressure air moves up the mountain or valley side, while the cooler mountain air from the shady side slides in under it. At night the land cools rapidly, creating high-pressure cold air, which sinks and moves down the mountain or valley sides, making it colder than the sides of the mountain.

6. Which side of a mountain is always driest?

 The leeward side is always driest.

7. Why do Californians call the Santa Ana an "ill wind"?

 Because people are said to do strange things when this screaming, nerve-racking, hot, dry wind blows and blows.

8. Explain the process that creates a monsoon.

 During summer the land areas are strongly heated by the sun. The air expands and rises, creating a low-pressure area. The oceans are naturally cooler, creating a high-pressure area. The high-pressure area slides in under the low-pressure area, creating the summer monsoons. Coming off the oceans, the summer monsoon brings rain to the continent. The winter monsoon is exactly the opposite. The land is cooler than the oceans. Winds blow from the interior of the continent onto the oceans, bringing cold dry air.

9. Why doesn't North America have a strong monsoonal pattern?

 North America doesn't have a very strong monsoon system due to the location of coastal mountain ranges on both the east and west sides of our continent and the direction of our prevailing westerlies. There is not much land for the winds to cross before they hit the coastal mountains, drop their moisture and create dry areas on the leeward side.

Vocabulary

1. **chinook**: a warm, dry wind flowing down the dry eastern sides of the Rockies. Creates dangerous early thawing of rivers and lakes.
2. **foehn**: rapidly moving warm, dry air on the leeward side of the Alps. The warmth is due to the drop in altitude. This is the adiabatic rate for descending air! For every 1,000-foot *decrease* in elevation, there will be a 3.5°F *rise* in temperature.
3. **monsoon**: a seasonal wind in southern Asia and the Indian Ocean region that blows from the ocean onto the land in the summer and down from the mountains during winter. The summer monsoons bring rainfall, while the winter monsoons are very dry.

Lesson 38

Review Statements

1. Highland climates can be found anywhere on the planet that has areas of high elevation.
2. Climate changes according to elevation, becoming cooler as elevation increases.
3. Mt. Kilimanjaro is the highest mountain in the world open to hikers.

Review Questions (page 221)

1. Using information from earlier lessons explain why temperatures drop as you increase in elevation.

 According to the adiabatic rate, temperatures drop 3.5°F with an increase in altitude of 1,000 feet; the molecules expand in the colder air.

2. In your own words discuss the formation of glaciers, the climate that is favorable to their formation and why they melt and recede.

 Glaciers form at high elevations where there is enough precipitation to produce snow, but where it is cold enough that the snow does not melt.

VOCABULARY
1. **tierra caliente:** a zone of hot temperatures, dense vegetation and tropical agriculture.
2. **tierra templada:** a temperate zone, with mild temperatures both day and night.
3. **tierra fria:** a cold land with warm days and cold nights.
4. **tierra helada:** a zone of snow, ice, and cold temperatures year-round.
5. **recede:** to move back or away.

LESSON 39

REVIEW STATEMENTS
1. There are four distinct layers of the atmosphere: the troposphere, stratosphere, mesosphere, and thermosphere.
2. The troposphere is closest to us and contains almost all the particles and water vapor that create our weather and climate.
3. The stratosphere is above the troposphere and absorbs harmful radiation.
4. The mesosphere is above the stratosphere and has the lowest temperatures in the atmosphere.
5. The thermosphere is above the mesosphere and is the outermost layer of our atmosphere.
6. The thermosphere absorbs solar radiation and has the highest temperatures in the atmosphere.
7. The jet stream runs through the troposphere.
8. Pollution of the atmosphere is one of our major concerns today.

REVIEW QUESTIONS (PAGE 228)
1. When is it possible to see air?
    You can see air only when it contains particles, such as dust, smoke, pollution, or water.
2. What determines wind direction?
    The place on the planet determines wind direction.
3. What are the four distinct layers of the atmosphere?
    The troposphere, stratosphere, mesosphere, and thermosphere.
4. Which layer is the coldest? Why?
    The mesosphere is the coldest, because it absorbs little solar energy.
5. Which layer is the hottest? Why?
    The thermosphere is the hottest, because it absorbs tremendous amounts of solar radiation.
6. Which layer is the weather layer?
    The troposphere is the weather layer.
7. In which layer do pilots prefer to fly? Why?
    Pilots prefer to fly in the stratosphere because there is little moisture, dust, or turbulence.
8. List the two jet streams and explain how they effect our weather.
    The two jet streams are the subpolar and the subtropical. The subpolar plays the dominant role in our weather. During winter, the subpolar jet stream reaches all the way into the southern states, bringing cold arctic air. In summer, it generally stays up in Canada, allowing warm air from the subtropical jet stream to move northward, bringing warmer temperatures and moist air. Because the subtropical low is comparatively weak and our continent so big, the subtropical jet stream doesn't penetrate very far inland.

9. How much of the sun's energy actually reaches the earth's surface?
    70%
10. Discuss the role of albedo in heating and cooling our atmosphere.

Albedo is the reflection rate of solar energy. The amount of solar heat reflected depends on cloud cover, particles in the atmosphere, extent of snow and vegetation on the earth's surface, and shiny objects that reflect the heat back into space. If less solar energy is reflected because of changes in these factors, then the atmosphere will become hotter. If more solar energy is reflected, then the atmosphere will become colder.

VOCABULARY

1. **troposphere**: the lower layer of the atmosphere.
2. **climate**: the average weather over an extended period of time.
3. **weather**: the daily changes in climate, such as a rainy day.
4. **subpolar**: below the polar region.
5. **subtropical**: adjacent to the tropics.
6. **stratosphere**: the second layer of the atmosphere, above the troposphere and below the mesosphere. It is layered and is the region where ozone is absorbed.
7. **mesosphere**: the third layer of the atmosphere, between the stratosphere and the thermosphere. It has the lowest temperatures in the atmosphere.
8. **thermosphere**: the outermost layer of the atmosphere. It absorbs solar radiation and has the highest temperatures in the atmosphere. There is no limit to its outer boundaries.
9. **albedo**: the reflection rate of solar energy.
10. **Bedouins**: nomadic Arabs of the Arabian, Syrian and North African deserts.

Chapter 9 Review   The Biosphere

LESSON 40

REVIEW STATEMENTS
1. The biosphere is the part of the world in which life can exist.
2. The basic ingredients of soil are organic materials, inorganic materials, water, and air.
3. Chemical and physical weathering help to create soil.
4. Coarse soil is classified as sand.
5. Fine soil is silt.
6. The finest soil is clay.
7. A pedologist is a person who studies soil.
8. Pollution of the atmosphere is one of our major concerns today.

REVIEW QUESTIONS (PAGE 234)
1. Through which states does the continental divide pass?

   The continental divide passes through Montana, Wyoming, Idaho, Colorado, and New Mexico.

2. What kind of weather can you expect from a high-pressure air mass? A low-pressure mass?

   A high-pressure air mass will bring relatively cooler weather because cooler air has higher pressure. High pressure usually means clear skies and stable weather. A low-pressure air mass will bring relatively warmer temperatures. Low pressure means unstable air, perhaps bringing clouds and rain.

3. What are the basic ingredients, or recipe, for soil?

   Soil is made up of organic material, inorganic material, water, and air.

4. What physical forces might cause weathering to occur in large rocks in cooler climates?

   Wind, water, glacial erosion, freezing and expanding, tectonic stresses, and even tree roots and plants cause weathering.

5. How do the physical forces of erosion create such smooth and rounded rocks as seen in the house in Taos?

   The rocks rub against each other and against other hard matter, smoothing off their sharp edges.

6. What causes materials to decompose more quickly in tropical climates?

   Moisture and warmth speed up decomposition.

7. List the three classifications of soil.

   The three classifications of soil are sand, silt, and clay.

8. List and describe each layer of soil.

   The O horizon is the top layer of decomposing vegetation that is found in areas where there is a lot of natural vegetation.

   The A horizon, or topsoil, right below the O horizon, is most important for the growth of vegetation, with a good mixture of organic and inorganic materials.

   The B horizon is mostly composed of inorganic, or rock, material. It may include clay particles that make it dense and thick.

   The C horizon comes next. Here we find rock that is weathering, but is not yet small enough to help form soil.

   The R horizon is the solid rock that is the parent material.

9. How do soil layers become mixed together?

Some rocks may have been bent and folded, some tilted upright and others broken apart. Another way the layers are mixed up is by the creatures that live in the ground, such as earthworms, that move the soil up and down as they burrow, aerating it and fertilizing it for plants. Plants also help mix soil by reaching their roots into crevices, gradually breaking apart rock material and bringing nutrients up from lower horizons for food.

10. Give an example of physical and chemical weathering.

Water freezing in cracks, wind or water eroding the material, and glaciers sliding over the materials are all examples of physical weathering. An example of chemical weathering is when the minerals in rocks react with moisture and heat to change the material.

11. In which climate zone is soil is made in the shortest amount of time?

Soil is made most rapidly in moist and warm climates, near the equator.

12. Why is chemical weathering more important for soil development near the equator?

Near the equator, where the air is moist and there is plenty of water, chemical weathering is the most important. Minerals in rocks react with the warm water and air more easily than with cold.

13. Discuss ways to keep the soil from eroding.

Some ways to keep the soil from eroding are: planting different vegetation to keep the soil from washing away; practicing land conservation; using better farming methods; and planting trees to act as wind blocks.

VOCABULARY

1. **biosphere**: the part of the world in which life can exist.
2. **inorganic**: having origins in plant or animal matter.
3. **organic**: having origins in living organisms.
4. **weathering**: the physical and chemical breakdown of rocks and minerals at or near the earth's surface.
5. **physical weathering**: the breaking down of large rocks by freezing, thawing, wind, water, tectonic stresses, and even tree roots.
6. **chemical weathering**: chemical changes in rock materials as they interact with water, air, and decaying matter.
7. **oxidize**: to combine with oxygen.
8. **parent material**: basic rock material from which soil is made through the weathering process.
9. **decompose**: to break down through chemical change. When leaves rot they are decomposing.
10. **sand**: coarse, grainy material resulting from the disintegration of rocks.
11. **silt**: fine, loose soil that is deposited either by wind or water.
12. **clay**: very fine sedimentary particles.
13. **aerate**: to fill with air.
14. **bacteria**: microorganisms in the soil that decompose matter and help create more soil.
15. **salinization**: the process of increasing the salt content of soil. This occurs in areas of flooding, high evaporation, or over-watering, and it ruins the soil.
16. **pedologist**: a person who studies soil.

LESSON 41

REVIEW STATEMENTS
1. Climate is the long-term average weather for a region.
2. Weather is the short-term average for a region.
3. The major factors that determine the climate of a place on Earth include 1) latitude, 2) prevailing winds and rainfall, 3) location on the continent, 4) landforms, such as mountains and lakes, and 5) elevation.

REVIEW QUESTIONS (PAGE 239)
1. What is the Coriolis effect?

   The Coriolis effect is the effect created when the earth spins to the east, creating wind by its movement.
2. What determines wind direction?

   The place on the planet determines wind direction.
3. If someone told you to find 112° N, what would you say?

   Parallels of latitude only go to 90° N or S. There is no 112° N.
4. What is the difference between weather and climate?

   Weather is the short-term average for a region, such as what happens on a day-to-day basis. Climate is the long-term average weather for a region. Rainy weather means it is raining today. Rainy climate means it rains frequently throughout the year in the area.
5. With its monsoon winds, what is India's climate?

   The climate is tropical.
6. At approximately what latitude are most of the world's major deserts?

   Most of the world's deserts are located near 30° N and S latitude.
7. List the five major factors that determine the climate of a place.

   They are 1) latitude, 2) prevailing winds and rainfall, 3) location on the continent, 4) landforms, such as mountains and lakes, and 5) elevation.
8. Describe the climate where you live and decide in which climate region you live.

VOCABULARY
1. **climate**: the average weather for a region.
2. **weather**: the daily change in climate.
3. **elevation**: height above sea level (altitude and elevation have the same definition).

LESSON 42

REVIEW STATEMENTS
1. Erosion is an ongoing force of nature.
2. Water is the greatest agent of change on Earth.
3. Desertification is the process of productive land losing its fertility due to overuse, overgrazing, removal of land cover, and salinization.

REVIEW QUESTIONS (PAGE 243)

1. Draw a globe and label the tropical, temperate, and polar zones.
2. What is convection?

    Convection is the transfer of heat from one place to another by the movement of heated particles of gas or a liquid.
3. How much fresh water is readily available for use?

    Only 0.40%.
4. Where do the rays of the sun always shine most directly?

    The sun's rays always shine most directly in the tropics.
5. What is the greatest force for erosion?

    Water is the greatest force for erosion.
6. Why haven't the forces of erosion worn our planet flat?

    Because plate tectonics continually change the face of the continents, thrusting up huge blocks of crust while causing others to sink, all the while creating new crust.
7. Give examples of wind and fire erosion.

    An example of wind erosion is the erosion that took place during the dust bowl. An example of fire erosion is when fire destroys living vegetation, leaving the land bare and subject to erosion by wind and water.
8. Describe two ways people can stop the erosion of soil.

    People can use plants adapted to the environment to keep the soil from eroding. Terracing farmland can stop erosion on a hill or mountainside.
9. How can farmers use legumes to help the soil?

    Legumes bear nodules on the roots that contain nitrogen-fixing bacteria.
10. Think about where you live. List some areas that show signs of erosion.

LESSON 42 VOCABULARY

1. **desertification**: the process of productive land losing its fertility due to overuse, overgrazing, removal of land cover, and salinization.

HANDS-ON ACTIVITY (PAGES 244-245)

1. 48,52° N, 220° E	Paris, France - 1:00 p.m.
2. 52.31° N, 13.20° E	Berlin, Germany - 1:00 p.m.
3. 53.20° N, 6.15° W	Dublin, Ireland - 12:00 p.m.
4. 30.03° N, 31.15° E	Cairo, Egypt - 2:00 p.m.
5 41.49° N, 87.37° W	Chicago, Illinois - 6:00 a.m.
6. 22.32° N, 88.22° E	Calcutta, India - 4:30 p.m.
7. 40.43° N, 74.01° W	New York, New York - 7:00 a.m.
8. 19.24° N, 99.09° W	Mexico City, Mexico - 6:00 a.m.
9. 55.45° N, 37.37° E	Moscow, Russia - 3:00 p.m.
10. 34.03° N, 118.15° W	Los Angeles, California - 4:00 a.m.
11. 40.24° N, 3.41° W	Madrid, Spain - 1:00 p.m.
12. 41.52° N, 12.37° E	Rome, Italy - 1:00 p.m.
13. 33.55° S, 151.17° E	Sydney, Australia - 9:00 p.m
14. 35.42° N, 139.46° E	Tokyo, Japan - 8:00 p.m
15. 32.45° N, 96.48° W	Dallas, Texas - 6:00 a.m.

Do any of the days change? Why?

No, because we do not cross the International Date Line.

LESSON 43

REVIEW QUESTIONS
1. Plants adapt to different climate conditions.
2. A climax community is a biome where everything is perfectly balanced.
3. Eighty percent of the earth's land surface is covered with trees, grasses, and mosses.
4. Transpiration is the process by which plants sweat through their leaves.

LESSON 43 REVIEW QUESTIONS (PAGE 252)
1. List the five major factors that determine the climate of a place.
    They are 1) latitude, 2) prevailing winds and rainfall, 3) location on the continent, 4) landforms, such as mountains and lakes, and 5) elevation.
2. List the three classifications of soil.
    The three soil classifications are sand, silt, and clay.
3. List the four spheres of Earth.
    The lithosphere, hydrosphere, atmosphere, and biosphere.
4. What conditions must be exactly right for plants to be in a climax community?
    You must have the right vegetation for the amount of moisture, the right number of plants for the size of the area, the right oxygen-carbon dioxide balance, and the right recycling of waste and resources.
5. What kinds of events might cause a climax community to become more like a desert?
    Natural events like floods, fires, and drought, or human forces like farming, flooding with dams, mining, and polluting an area could all cause a climax community to become more like a desert.
6. List the four items plants need to survive.
    Plants need water, soil, carbon dioxide, and sunlight.
7. How have conifers adapted to cold climates?
    Conifers have thick, needlelike leaves to reduce the loss of moisture and insulate against extreme temperatures. They grow slowly and react slowly to environmental changes that might kill other plants.
8. How have mangrove trees adapted to watery climates?
    They have shallow roots and low branches to support the trunk, and they turn their large leaves toward the sun to increase transpiration.
9. How have cacti adapted to hot, desert climates?
    Cacti have developed extensive root systems to gather available moisture, and they store moisture internally. They grow slowly and have thick outer layers. They don't have leaves, so they loose less moisture through transpiration. They have developed grooves of spiny, thick skin to provide some shade for themselves. Cacti with small leaves turn the edges of their leaves toward the sun to reduce transpiration.

Vocabulary

1. **biome:** a major community characterized by its plant life and climate.
2. **climax community:** a biome where everything is perfectly balanced.
3. **taiga:** the northern coniferous forest, made up of spruce, fir, and pine trees.
4. **transpiration:** the process by which plants sweat through their leaves.
5. **xerophytes:** plants that have adapted to dry climates.
6. **hygrophytes:** plants that have adapted to very wet conditions.
7. **tropophytes:** plants that can adjust to the weather as it changes.
8. **mesophytes:** plants that do not have to tolerate extremes.
9. **maritime climate:** a climate influenced by nearness to sea or ocean.
10. **continental climate:** a climate within a large continent without the modifying influence of water.

Critical Thinking Activity (page 255)

Use the map of world crops (Fig. 9-37) to answer the following questions:

1. What is the highest parallel of latitude where crops are grown? The lowest?

   The highest is 65° N and the lowest is 45° S.

2. Where are the majority of crops grown?

   The majority of crops are grown between 30° and 60° N.

3. What are those crops?

   Wheat, corn, oats, rice, citrus, and potatoes.

4. Why are there no crops grown at 60°S?

   It is too far south, and there is no land at 60° S.

5. Which crops are grown the farthest north or south of the equator?

   Oats is grown the farthest north of the equator. Corn is grown the farthest south of the equator.

6. Which crops are grown at the equator?

   Wheat, corn, oats, rice, and citrus.

7. Where is the majority of rice grown?

   The majority of rice is grown in Asia between 15° and 45° N.

8. What physical features keep crops from growing in middle Africa, Australia, and South America?

   Mountains and deserts prevent crops from being grown in these areas.

9. What types of crops are best grown on the islands shown?

   Rice, corn, citrus, and oats.

10. Where are most citrus crops grown?

    Most citrus crops are grown between 45° N and 30° S.

11. Are there any continents with no crops grown? At what latitudes?

    Yes, crops are not grown in Antarctica. It is below 60° S in the Antarctic Circle.

LESSON 44

REVIEW STATEMENTS
1. There are only four categories of vegetation: desert, grassland, forest and tundra.
2. Plants must adapt to their environments or die out.

REVIEW QUESTIONS (PAGE 259)
1. Look outside and notice what kinds of trees are growing. Are they deciduous trees that lose their leaves in the fall? Are they coniferous evergreens with needles that stay green year-round?
2. Do flowers bloom at a certain time of the year where you live? When?
3. Think about the seasons in your area. When does spring arrive? How can you tell it is spring?
4. How can you tell when it is summer? Do any of the plants and trees change their appearance?
5. What happens in the fall where you live?
6. How early and how often does it snow where you live?
7. Does the ground freeze hard and the landscape become bleak and gray during winter where you live?
8. If Jack lived in your area when would be the best time for his mother to throw the beans out the window?
9. What is the difference between a hygrophyte and a xerophyte? Do either of these types of plants grow in your area?
10. What type of vegetation would you expect to find in the grasslands? Now think this through. Don't just answer grass. There is more to the answer than that.

Grasslands have the most fertile soil in the world, and are located in the middle latitudes where the majority of crops are grown, so you will find wheat, oats, corn, barley, and many other food crops in addition to grasses.
11. If you were a rattlesnake could you live on tundra or in a marsh?

    No. Rattlesnakes need warm dry weather to live.
12. Explain the statement, "The sun never sets on the British Empire." Use an encyclopedia and history books to find the answer.

    The British Empire at one time reached around the world, so that the sun was always shining on some part of the Empire.

VOCABULARY
1. **desert:** a region with less than ten inches of precipitation per year and having extremes in temperature.
2. **xerophytes:** plants that have adapted to dry climates
3. **grassland:** a climate zone with vegetation consisting chiefly of grasses. Found on steppes, prairies, pampas, meadows, velds and savannas.
4. **forest:** a climate zone consisting primarily of trees.
5. **tundra:** a mostly flat, treeless plain covered with lichens and mosses, having a marshy topsoil with a permanently frozen subsoil (permafrost); found in arctic and subarctic regons.
6. **hygrophytes:** plants that have adapted to very wet conditions.

Notes

Chapter Tests

Chapter 1 Test   Our Planet Earth

1. _____ is the largest island in the world.
   A. Madagascar
   B. Greenland
   C. Iceland
   D. New Guinea

2. What body of water separates Africa and Europe?
   A. Mediterranean Sea
   B. Sea of Cortez
   C. Pacific Ocean
   D. Indian Ocean

3. The zone of transition between light and dark around a sphere is called a_____.
   A. zone of light
   B. sun spot
   C. circle of illumination
   D. temperate zone

4. One of the seven principle land masses on earth is a/an _____.
   A. island
   B. mountain
   C. continent
   D. peninsula

5. A/An _____ is an imaginary pole that passes through the earth, connecting the North and South Poles.
   A. orbit
   B. axle
   C. axis
   D. shaft

6. Which continent has a horn?
   A. Africa
   B. Asia
   C. Antarctica
   D. North America

7. How far is Spain from Morocco at the Strait of Gibraltar?
   A. 7 miles
   B. 8 miles
   C. 12 miles
   D. 3 miles

8. Where does North America lie in relation to South America?
   A. northeast
   B. southeast
   C. northwest
   D. southwest

9. List the nine planets.

10. Which of the nine planets are terrestrial? Which are Jovian?

11. List the cardinal directions.

12. Which ocean is the largest?

13. List the seven continents from the largest to the smallest.

14. Which two continents appear to be one?

15. The earth is in which galaxy?

16. Using a blank sheet of paper draw the equator, prime meridian, and the seven continents in their relative locations.

17. Explain how centrifugal force maintains the balance of our solar system. Can you name some times when you have experienced the pull of centrifugal force?

18. Draw a compass rose and plot the cardinal and intermediate directions.

19. Is there more than one sun in the Milky Way?

20. Can there be more than one solar system in a galaxy?

Matching:

Write the letter of the correct definition in the space before each term.

_____ 21. asteroid   A. a large luminous ball of gas that is held together by its own gravity.

_____ 22. axis   B. all that exists.

_____ 23. galaxy   C. system containing stars, nebulae, star clusters, etc.

_____ 24. island   D. a complete turn around an axis or point.

_____ 25. light year   E. 5.88 trillion miles.

_____ 26. ocean   F. the sun and everything that orbits around the sun.

_____ 27. orbit   G. the path taken by a body in space as it moves around its center of attraction.

_____ 28. revolution   H. an imaginary pole that passes through the earth, connecting the North and South Poles.

_____ 29. sea   I. a celestial body that is a few feet to several hundred miles across and has a distinct orbit.

_____ 30. solar system   J. any landmass smaller than a continent that is completely surrounded by water.

_____ 31. star   K. the body of salt water that covers 70% of the earth's surface and is divided into five primary divisions.

_____ 32. universe   L. a body of water smaller than an ocean.

Chapter 2 Test   Maps and Their Uses

1. A _____ is the most accurate representation of the earth.
   A. map
   B. photograph
   C. globe
   D. graph

2. There are _____ decimeters in a meter.
   A. 5
   B. 10
   C. 7
   D. 100

3. The sea near the middle of the Atlantic Ocean is the _____.
   A. Center Sea
   B. Aral Sea
   C. Red Sea
   D. Sargasso Sea

4. One of the seven principle land masses on earth is a/an _____.
   A. island
   B. mountain
   C. continent
   D. peninsula

5. A _____ is the representation of the earth on a flat surface.
   A. globe
   B. diagram
   C. graph
   D. map projection

6. An azimuthal projection that is centered on one of the poles is a _____.
   A. Mercator projection
   B. Robinson projection
   C. Goode projection
   D. polar projection

7. An imaginary line that circles the earth and divides it into two equal parts is called a/an _____.
   A. equator
   B. parallel of latitude
   C. line of longitude
   D. great circle

8. A _____ is a person who draws maps.
   A. cartographer
   B. globe trotter
   C. geographer
   D. geologist

9. How is a Mercator map distorted?

10. List the five major oceans.

11. What problems do cartographers face in drawing the earth?

12. Where does distortion become greatest on a map?

13. How is a polar projection limited in its use?

14. One kilometer is equal to .62 miles. How many kilometers are there in 7 miles?

15. What keeps Antarctica the "frozen continent"?

16. Which map projection shows you the true shape of Antarctica?

17. Write a paragraph describing different ways to use large scale and small scale maps.

18. List and define the five basic parts of a map.

Matching:

Write the letter of the correct definition in the space before each term.

_____ 19. azimuthal

_____ 20. compromise

_____ 21. conformal map

_____ 22. distortion

_____ 23. Gerhardus Mercator

_____ 24. Goode projection

_____ 25. projection

_____ 26. quest

_____ 27. simultaneous

_____ 28. three-dimensional

A. a search or pursuit made in order to find or obtain something.

B. having height, width, and depth.

C. occurring at the same time.

D. a system by which lines of latitude and longitude are drawn onto a planar or flat surface so as to represent the curved surface of the earth.

E. an agreement reached where those involved give up something.

F. the state of being twisted or stretched out of shape.

G. a map that maintains the true shapes of landmasses but not the sizes.

H. a circular projection that shows one-half of the globe.

I. a projection of Earth in which certain portions of the oceans are removed.

J. the first cartographer to name both North and South America.

Chapter 3 Test   Latitude and Climate

1. Hemi- means _____.
   A. full
   B. all
   C. two
   D. half

2. The numerical value of latitude at the equator is _____.
   A. 90°
   B. 30°
   C. 0°
   D. 23.5°

3. One rotation of the earth equals _____ day/s.
   A. 1
   B. 365 1/4
   C. 360
   D. 31

4. One revolution of the earth around the sun equals _____ day/s?
   A. 1
   B. 365 1/4
   C. 360
   D. 31

5. The tropic of Cancer is found at what parallel of latitude?
   A. 23.5° S
   B. 30° N
   C. 23.5° N
   D. 30° S

6. Low latitudes have _____ temperatures.
   A. low
   B. moderate
   C. high
   D. cold

7. The earth is at _____ when it is closest to the sun.
   A. aphelion
   B. equinox
   C. perihelion
   D. ellipse

8. The _____ divides the earth into halves forming the Northern and Southern Hemispheres.
   A. parallel
   B. equinox
   C. arctic circle
   D. equator

9. Which calendar do we use today?
   A. Egyptian
   B. lunar
   C. Gregorian
   D. Julian

10. Where will you find the middle latitudes?

11. Why do the high latitudes have low temperatures?

12. Why do the low latitudes have high temperatures?

13. Which direction does the earth spin in its rotation?

14. Explain "land of the midnight sun."

Matching:

Write the letter of the correct definition in the space before each term.

_____ 15. axis

_____ 16. North Pole

_____ 17. latitude

_____ 18. summer solstice

_____ 19. correlation

_____ 20. South Pole

_____ 21. conversely

_____ 22. ellipse

_____ 23. parallel

_____ 24. middle latitudes

A. remaining an equal distance apart at all times and at all points.

B. distance north or south of the equator.

C. 90° north latitude, the northernmost point on the globe.

D. 90° south latitude, the southernmost point on the globe.

E. the areas between 30° and 60° north and south of the equator.

F. a complimentary, reciprocal relationship between two or more things.

G. an imaginary pole that passes through the earth, connecting the North and South Poles.

H. in the opposite way.

I. an elongated circle, or oval.

J. June 21st, the day when the sun's rays are as far north of the equator as they will ever be.

Chapter 4 Test   Prime Time Longitude

1. _____ are not parallel.
   - A. prime meridian
   - B. meridians of longitude
   - C. lines of latitude
   - D. lines of circumference

2. If you move west of the prime meridian you _____ in time.
   - A. increase
   - B. decrease
   - C. don't change
   - D. lose one day

3. A line extending from pole to pole that measures longitude is called a/an _____.
   - A. tropic
   - B. equator
   - C. meridian
   - D. line of latitude

4. What units are used on maps to give directions that are more specific than degrees?
   - A. minutes and seconds
   - B. days and hours
   - C. months and years
   - D. light years

5. _____ is the location according to latitude and longitude.
   - A. standard location
   - B. absolute location
   - C. location of latitude
   - D. exact location

6. _____ is based directly on the sun's position.
   - A. Greenwich Mean Time
   - B. standard time
   - C. daylight savings time
   - D. sun time

7. The International Date Line generally follows which meridian? _____.
   - A. 180° N
   - B. 180° S
   - C. 180°
   - D. 170°

8. Ante meridian means _____.
   - A. after the meridian
   - B. during the meridian
   - C. before the meridian
   - D. against the meridian

9. If you wanted to draw a map for the purpose of telling time, how many degrees apart would you draw your meridians?
    A. 30°
    B. 15°
    C. 10°
    D. 24°

10. Does the time change along the same meridian of longitude as you move from the Northern to the Southern Hemisphere? Be specific in your answer.

11. Is the International Date Line a straight line? Please explain your answer.

12. How many time zones are there in the United States?

13. How many time zones are there in Canada?

14. Do both countries have the same times? Be specific in your answer.

15. What is the purpose of daylight saving time?

Matching:

Write the letter of the correct definition in the space before each term.

_____ 16. merge

A. a measurement of time that is directly based on the position of the sun.

_____ 17. circumference

B. the mean or average time established at the meridian in Greenwich, England which is used as the basis for determining time worldwide.

_____ 18. sun time

C. to unite, blend or come together.

_____ 19. GMT

D. the 0° meridian from which all longitude is measured east and west, passing through Greenwich, England, site of the Royal Observatory.

_____ 20. prime meridian

E. the outer boundary of a circular area.

Use the World Map to locate the referenced cities, and then use the Time Zone Chart to answer the following questions.

21. If it is 3:00 P.M. on Monday in Mexico City, Mexico, (99.09° W), what time and day is it in Cairo, Egypt, (31.17° E)?

22. If it is 7:00 A.M. on Friday in Berlin, Germany, (13.28° E), what time is it in New York City, New York (73.58° W)?

23. If it is 11:00 A.M. on Tuesday in Sydney, Australia, (151.17° E), what time and day is it in Los Angeles, CA (118,14° W)?

24. If it is 10:00 P.M. on Wednesday in Calcutta, India, (88.28° E), what time is it in Moscow, Russia (37.37° E)?

25. How many hours separate Chicago, Illinois, (87.37° W) from New York City, New York (73.58° W)?

26. How many hours separate Dallas, Texas, (96.48° W) from Rome, Italy (12.37° E)?

27. How many hours separate Tokyo, Japan, (139.46° E) and Seattle, Washington (122.20° W)?

28. How many hours difference is there between Los Angeles (118.14° W) and New York City (73.58° W)?

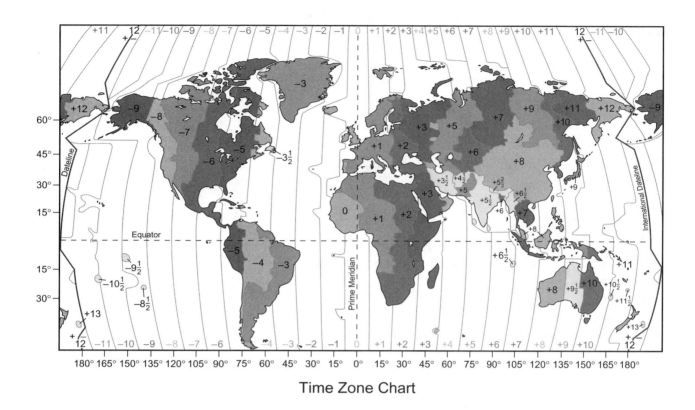

Time Zone Chart

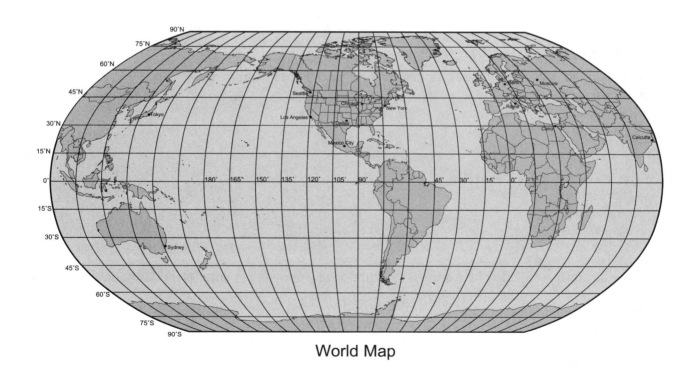

World Map

Chapter 5 Test   Journey to the Center of the Earth
(The Lithosphere)

1. The crust is the _____ layer of the earth.
   A. middle
   B. bottom
   C. top
   D. inner

2. Molten material beneath the earth's crust is called _____.
   A. magma
   B. lava
   C. liquid rock
   D. mantle

3. _____ is/are used to map the ocean floor.
   A. sonar
   B. radar
   C. sea charts
   D. Richter scale

4. Which of the following is not a way in which tectonic plates react?
   A. converge
   B. diverge
   C. divulge
   D. strike-slip

5. The _____ is the innermost layer of the earth, occupying a fifth of our planet's volume.
   A. mantle
   B. crust
   C. core
   D. Moho

6. According to scientists, the earth's core should be made of what material?
   A. solid rock
   B. liquid rock
   C. nickel-iron alloy
   D. ice

7. The upper mantle is called the _____.
   A. lithosphere
   B. asthenosphere
   C. biosphere
   D. crust

8. The point on the surface of the earth lying immediately above the center of an earthquake is called the _____.
   A. quake zone
   B. equinox
   C. epicenter
   D. sediment

9. The highest point in the world is _____.
   A. Mount Whitney
   B. Mount Everest
   C. Mount Shasta
   D. Mount Rainier

10. The central 750 miles of the earth is the _____.
    A. asthenosphere
    B. Moho
    C. outer core
    D. inner core

11. The earth's crust is known as the _____.
    A. asthenosphere
    B. Moho
    C. lithosphere
    D. rift

12. List the four sections of the earth.

13. List two ways we know the interior of the earth is hot.

14. Why does oceanic crust subduct below continental crust?

15. What happens when two oceanic plates collide? What can result from this collision?

16. List and explain the three ways tectonic plates react when they collide.

17. What is the difference between the Mercalli and Richter scales?

Matching:

Write the letter of the correct definition in the space before each term.

_____ 18. Richter scale   A. the transfer of heat from one place to another by the movement of heated particles of gas or a liquid.

_____ 19. tsunami   B. crustal debris that has been deposited by wind, water, or ice.

_____ 20. fault   C. to separate. This occurs when two plates move apart.

_____ 21. alloy   D. a crack in the earth's bedrock along which movement has occurred.

_____ 22. Mid-Atlantic Ridge   E. the interaction of the crustal plates that produces earthquakes, volcanoes, and mountains while creating and destroying crust.

_____ 23. sediment   F. a measure of the severity of earthquakes, with each whole number increase indicating ten times more ground movement and about thirty times more energy.

_____ 24. subduction   G. a mixture of two or more metals.

_____ 25. plate tectonics   H. giant destructive waves created by undersea earthquakes or underwater landslides.

_____ 26. convection   I. huge rigid slabs of crust.

_____ 27. plates   J. a long, continuous underwater mountain range that lies roughly parallel to continental margins; formed by volcanic outpourings from the asthenosphere. The center is marked by a steep V.

_____ 28. converge   K. movement of the ocean floor beneath the continental crust.

_____ 29. diverge   L. to come together. This occurs when two plates come together and collide.

_____ 30. strike-slip   M. when one plate moves past another in an opposite direction involving very little change.

_____ 31. rift   N. the part attached to a base word.

_____ 32. Mercalli scale   O. the boundary between the lithosphere and asthenosphere.

_____ 33. suffix   P. able to rise or float in the air or on the surface of a liquid.

_____ 34. Moho   Q. an arbitrary ranking of earthquake destruction based on observations of survivors.

_____ 35. buoyant   R. a tear in the earth's crust.

Chapter 6 Test   Mountain Building

1. _____ is the process of building mountains.
   - A. origami
   - B. orogenesis
   - C. cordillera
   - D. convection

2. A _____ consists of a series of more or less parallel mountain ranges.
   - A. mountain
   - B. mountain system
   - C. shield
   - D. trench

3. Movement of the oceanic plate beneath the continental crust is called _____.
   - A. subduction
   - B. obduction
   - C. accretion
   - D. collision

4. The _____ divide/s Europe from Asia.
   - A. San Andreas fault
   - B. Rocky Mountains
   - C. Himalayan Mountains
   - D. Ural Mountains

5. Which continent does not have either active or extinct volcanoes?
   - A. Asia
   - B. Australia
   - C. Antarctica
   - D. Africa

6. The pushing of two plates of the earth's crust against each other to form mountains is called _____.
   - A. subduction
   - B. obduction
   - C. accretion
   - D. collision

7. The Greek word oros means _____.
   - A. raise
   - B. push
   - C. land
   - D. mountain

8. Pyros is a Greek word meaning _____.
   - A. water
   - B. heat
   - C. fire
   - D. rock

9. The _____ divide/s the North American plate from the Pacific plate.
   A. Olympic Mountains
   B. San Andreas fault
   C. Cascades
   D. Rocky Mountains

10. _____ occurs when seafloor sediment becomes attached to the overriding continental crust.
   A. Subduction
   B. Obduction
   C. Accretion
   D. Collision

11. What is the difference between a mountain range and a cordillera?

12. List and explain the four ways in which mountains are formed.

13. List the three kinds of volcanoes and explain how each is formed.

14. What is the difference between a geyser and a hot spring?

15. What was the importance of the Cumberland Gap in the Appalachian mountains?

16. The San Andreas fault divides which two plates?

17. Why are island arcs found only in oceans?

18. Why do government officials on Montserrat fear volcano education has had a negative effect on safety?

19. What is a seamount? How can it be considered both the beginning and end of an island?

20. Why do the Ural Mountains extend in a N-S direction?

Matching:

Write the letter of the correct definition in the space before each term.

_____ 21. seam

A. a long, narrow depression in the sea floor, produced by bending of oceanic crust during subduction.

_____ 22. shield

B. ancient block of continental crust that has been tectonically stable for a lengthy geologic timespan.

_____ 23. trench

C. magma that cools and hardens in cold water.

_____ 24. Pamir Knot

D. a series of mountain ridges closely related in direction and position.

_____ 25. Ring of Fire

E. volcanic mountains encircling the Pacific Ocean.

_____ 26. Aa

F. a mountain pass or opening made by a break in the mountains.

_____ 27. Pahoehoe

G. the process of building mountains.

_____ 28. caldera

H. thick, gooey lava with chunks of rock in it.

_____ 29. mountain range

I. a large depression caused by the collapse of the summit area of a volcano.

_____ 30. hot spot

J. a sharp and steep-sided surface area at least three hundred meters above the surrounding land surface.

_____ 31. gap

K. the point where two plates come together and are joined.

_____ 32. cinder cone

L. a highland region of south central Asia rising up to 24,540 feet (7,500 m).

_____ 33. mountain

M. geologically young hills or mountains composed of loose pyroclastic materials that easily erode.

_____ 34. pillow lava

N. lava that is ropy and smooth in texture.

_____ 35. orogenesis

O. a permanent place where intense heat from the mantle burns through the lithosphere.

Chapter 7 Test   The Hydrosphere

1. _____ is the average weather in a broad area over a specific period of time.
   A. weather
   B. climate
   C. precipitation
   D. isostasy

2. _____ is the greatest agent of change on the earth.
   A. wind
   B. water
   C. heat
   D. cold

3. What percent of all precipitation falls over the oceans?
   A. 50%
   B. 45%
   C. 75%
   D. 60%

4. The beginning of a river is called _____.
   A. frontwaters
   B. aquifer
   C. alluvial fans
   D. headwaters

5. Currents below the equator flow _____.
   A. clockwise
   B. counterclockwise
   C. north to south
   D. south to north

6. _____ is the ability of the planet to seek a state of equilibrium.
   A. balance
   B. equal ratio
   C. isostasy
   D. effluents

7. How much of the world's water is readily available for use?
   A. 5%
   B. 0.55%
   C. 0.40%
   D. 15%

8. Something that has openings or pores which allows water or gases to pass through is called
   _____.
   A. hollow
   B. an unconfined aquifer
   C. a confined aquifer
   D. permeable

9. _____ power/s the water cycle.
   A. wind currents
   B. gravity
   C. the sun
   D. Rocky Mountains

10. The _____ is the strongest of the world's cold ocean currents.
   A. California
   B. Labrador
   C. Humboldt
   D. Oyashio

11. A/An _____ is a river flowing with a larger body of water.
   A. current
   B. upwell
   C. Gulf Stream
   D. monsoon

12. _____ form in high latitudes and cover huge areas of land.
   A. continental glaciers
   B. alpine glaciers
   C. headwaters
   D. hanging valleys

13. Explain the water cycle.

14. Explain why there are deserts along the western coast of every continent except Europe.

15. List the four primary reasons precipitation falls where it does.

16. Explain why Antarctica is classified as a desert.

17. Why are the Appalachian Mountains not considered a continental divide?

18. What must happen in order for glaciers to develop?

19. Explain the adiabatic rate.

20. Why is the Humboldt current cold?

21. How does flooding damage the land? Be specific in your answer.

22. Explain why we should all be concerned about agricultural runoff into our rivers.

23. Why aren't there any deserts in Europe?

24. What does a mean annual precipitation map fail to tell us?

Matching:

Write the letter of the correct definition in the space before each term.

_____ 25. water table

A. the end of a river where it empties into a larger body of water.

_____ 26. desalination

B. a deep crack in a glacier due to movement.

_____ 27. trade wind

C. the upper limit of the water level when the ground is filled with water.

_____ 28. upwelling

D. a hot, dusty wind blowing from the Libyan desert of northern Africa.

_____ 29. weather

E. a warm ocean current flowing northward from the equator, skirting the eastern coasts of North America before turning eastward towards Europe.

_____ 30. sirocco

F. the process of removing salt from sea water.

_____ 31. mouth

G. very fine soil that is moved either by wind or water.

_____ 32. silt

H. a fan-shaped landform created when a river deposits alluvial soil onto a plain.

_____ 33. monsoon

I. the movement of deeper, cooler, nutrient-rich waters to the ocean surface.

_____ 34. Gulf Stream

J. the daily changes that occur in specific locations in the atmosphere.

_____ 35. terminal moraine

K. a seasonal wind in southern Asia and the Indian Ocean.

_____ 36. alluvial fan

L. an almost constant wind blowing in the same direction.

_____ 37. cirque

M. a sea of sand.

_____ 38. delta

N. a large mountain hollow created by a glacier.

_____ 39. crevasse

O. the final deposit of glacial debris marking the farthest advance of a glacier.

_____ 40. erg

P. sedimentary deposit extending beyond the mouth of a river where it empties into a lake or sea.

_____ 41. reg

Q. desert pavement.

Chapter 8 Test   The Atmosphere

1. Hot air rises and has _____ pressure.
   A. high
   B. low
   C. equal
   D. excessive

2. How much water the air can hold is called _____.
   A. relative humidity
   B. air pressure
   C. water level
   D. adiabatic rate

3. The _____ side of a mountain is always the driest.
   A. north
   B. south
   C. leeward
   D. windward

4. India receives its monsoon rains during the _____.
   A. spring
   B. summer
   C. winter
   D. fall

5. There are desert conditions at about _____ due to the sinking of cool and dry air.
   A. 60° N and S of the equator
   B. 65° N and S of the equator
   C. 30° N and S of the equator
   D. 45° N and S of the equator

6. The higher you go in the atmosphere the _____ the air pressure becomes.
   A. hotter
   B. lower
   C. higher
   D. colder

7. Which jet stream plays the dominant role in our weather?
   A. polar
   B. tropical
   C. subtropical
   D. subpolar

8. What determines wind direction?
   A. heat
   B. latitude
   C. place on the planet
   D. placement of mountains

9. How much of the sun's energy actually reaches the earth's surface?
   A. 20%
   B. 30%
   C. 80%
   D. 70%

10. _____ air holds the most water.
    A. cold
    B. hot
    C. polluted
    D. thin

11. Define the adiabatic rate and discuss how it affects air pressure.

12. What role do the southeast trade winds have in maintaining the Amazon Rain Forest?

13. List the four layers of the atmosphere in order from the closest to the farthest from the earth's surface. Beside each layer list a distinguishing characteristic of that layer.

14. Explain the process that creates a monsoon.

Matching:

Write the letter of the correct definition in the space before each term.

_____ 15. air pressure

_____ 16. front

_____ 17. acclimating

_____ 18. chinook

_____ 19. foehn

_____ 20. Coriolis effect

_____ 21. doldrums

_____ 22. becalmed

_____ 23. horse latitudes

_____ 24. trade winds

_____ 25. albedo

_____ 26. vortex

_____ 27. solar radiation

A. rapidly moving warm, dry air on the leeward side of the Alps.

B. an area where highs and lows meet often bringing severe weather.

C. a mass of swirling fluid.

D. when the earth spins to the east, creating wind by its movement.

E. 30° to 35° N and S. The calmest zones on Earth.

F. a warm, dry wind flowing down the dry eastern side of the Rockies.

G. unable to sail due to lack of wind.

H. the force air exerts on its surroundings due to its weight.

I. heat coming from the sun.

J. reflection rate of solar energy.

K. fairly constant winds blowing towards the equator from the high-pressure zones around 30° N or S.

L. an area of calm, also referred to as the "blues".

M. becoming accustomed to a new climate.

Chapter 9 Test   The Biosphere

1. A/an _____ is a person who studies soil.
   A. archeologist
   B. biologist
   C. pedologist
   D. sociologist

2. _____ is the process of land losing its fertility due to overuse, overgrazing, removal of land cover, and salinization.
   A. erosion
   B. desertification
   C. weathering
   D. oxidizing

3. A _____ is a biome where everything is perfectly balanced.
   A. climax community
   B. balanced environment
   C. biosphere
   D. biodome

4. What does water do when it freezes?
   A. shrink
   B. expand
   C. evaporate
   D. subduct

5. Which climate zone region does not fit into the patterns for most other regions?
   A. marine
   B. tropics
   C. lowlands
   D. highlands

6. _____ is the physical or chemical breakdown of rocks and minerals at or near the earth's surface.
   A. decomposition
   B. weathering
   C. oxidizing
   D. aerating

7. _____ is the primary source of energy for almost half of the world's people.
   A. oil
   B. nuclear power
   C. natural gas
   D. wood

8. What percentage of the earth's land is covered with trees, grasses, and mosses?
   A. 20%
   B. 80%
   C. 35%
   D. 75%

9. _____ are planted to revitalize the soil with vitamins needed by all plants.
    A. trees
    B. legumes
    C. cotton
    D. wheat

10. Which of the following is not a classification of soil?
    A. mud
    B. silt
    C. clay
    D. sand

11. What two things cause materials to decompose more quickly in tropical climates?

12. List and describe each layer of soil.

13. List the five major factors that determine the climate of a place.

14. List the four items that plants need to survive.

15. Why haven't the forces of erosion worn our planet flat?

16. What conditions must be exactly right for plants to be in a climax community?

Matching:

Write the letter of the correct definition in the space before each term.

_____ 17. inorganic

_____ 18. organic

_____ 19. oxidize

_____ 20. parent material

_____ 21. sand

_____ 22. silt

_____ 23. clay

_____ 24. taiga

_____ 25. transpiraton

_____ 26. xerophytes

_____ 27. hygrophytes

_____ 28. tropophytes

_____ 29. mesophytes

_____ 30. elevation

_____ 31. maritime climate

_____ 32. physical weathering

A. the process by which plants sweat through their leaves.

B. coarse, grainy material resulting from the disintegration of rocks.

C. plants that have adapted to very wet conditions.

D. not having origins from plant or animal matter.

E. very fine sedimentary particles.

F. plants that do not have to tolerate extremes.

G. the northern coniferous forest, made up of spruce, fir, and pine trees.

H. having origins in living organisms.

I. basic rock material from which soil is made.

J. climate influenced by nearness to a sea or ocean.

K. plants that have adapted to dry climates.

L. fine, loose soil that is deposited by either wind or water.

M. to combine with oxygen.

N. the breaking down of large rocks by freezing, thawing, wind, or water.

O. plants that can adjust to the weather as it changes.

P. height above sea level.

Notes

Chapter Tests
Answer Guide

Chapter 1 Test Answers   Our Planet Earth

1. B   2. A   3. C   4. C   5. C   6. A   7. B   8. C

9. List the nine planets.
> *Mercury, Venus, Earth, Mars, Jupiter, Saturn, Uranus, Neptune, Pluto*

10. Which of the nine planets are terrestrial? Which are Jovian?
> *Mercury, Venus, Earth, and Mars are terrestial. Jupiter, Saturn, Uranus, and Neptune are Jovian.*

11. List the cardinal directions.
> *North, east, south, and west.*

12. Which ocean is the largest?
> *The Pacific.*

13. List the seven continents from the largest to the smallest.
> *Asia, Africa, North America, South America, Antarctica, Europe, and Australia.*

14. Which two continents appear to be one?
> *Europe and Asia.*

15. The earth is in which galaxy?
> *The Milky Way.*

16. Using a blank sheet of paper draw the equator, prime meridian and the seven continents in their relative locations.
> *This drawing should look like the makeshift map.*

17. Explain how centrifugal force maintains the balance of our solar system.
> *The sun acts like a giant magnet pulling the planets toward itself. As the planets orbit, or move in a curved motion around the sun, their centrifugal force pushes them away from the center of the curve, which is the sun. The push of centrifugal force and the pull of the sun strike a balance, keeping the planets from being pulled into the sun or flying into space.*

18. Draw a compass rose and plot the cardinal and intermediate directions.
> *This should look similar to the compass rose on page 7 of the text.*

19. Is there more than one sun in the Milky Way?
> *Yes.*

20. Can there be more than one solar system in a galaxy?
> *Yes.*

Matching:

21. I   22. H   23. C   24. J   25. E   26. K

27. G   28. D   29. L   30. F   31. A   32. B

Chapter 2 Test Answers   Maps and Their Uses

1. C   2. B   3. D   4. C   5. D   6. D   7. D   8. A

9. How is a Mercator map distorted?

The size of the land masses becomes more distorted as you move from the equator toward the poles. Greenland is an example. It appears much larger than it actually is on a Mercator map.

10. List the five major oceans.

Pacific, Atlantic, Indian, Arctic, and Antarctic.

11. What problems do cartographers face in drawing the earth?

Drawing a three-dimensional object on a two-dimensional piece of paper. Deciding whether to draw accurate shape, size, distance, or direction.

12. Where does distortion become greatest on a map?

Distortion is greatest near the edges.

13. How is a polar projection limited in its use?

It can only be used to see either the Southern or Northern Hemisphere at one time. It won't allow you to see all of the Eastern or Western Hemispheres at one time.

14. One kilometer is equal to .62 miles. How many kilometers are there in seven miles?

Divide seven miles by .62 miles per kilometer to get 11.29 km.

15. What keeps Antarctica the "frozen continent?"

A single current of cold water completely encircles Antarctica preventing warm waters from reaching its shores.

16. Which map projection shows you the true shape of Antarctica?

The polar projection.

17. Write a paragraph describing different ways to use large scale and small scale maps.

A large scale map shows a large amount of detail about a small area. Some different uses for large scale maps are maps of neighborhoods, amusement parks, campgrounds, buildings, etc. Small scale maps show a small amount of detail about a large area. Some different uses for small scale maps are state, country, continental maps, etc.

18. List and define the five basic parts of a map.

Title: tells the reader the subject of the map.

Legend: shows colors, patterns, or symbols used on the map and what they represent.

Grid System: the interlocking set of lines established by parallels of latitude and meridians of longitude which is used to find an exact location.

Direction: shows the cardinal and/or intermediate directions on the map.

Scale: shows the size relationship of the items on the map using representative fractions.

Matching:

19. H   20. E   21. G   22. F   23. J

24. I   25. D   26. A   27. C   28. B

Chapter 3 Test Answers Latitude and Climate

1. D   2. C   3. A   4. B   5. C   6. C   7. C   8. D   9. C

10. Where will you find the middle latitudes?

The middle latitudes are between 30° and 60° north and south of the equator

11. Why do the high latitudes have low temperatures?

The high latitudes don't receive direct rays from the sun, so the temperature is lower than the areas of the earth that do receive direct rays.

12. Why do the low latitudes have high temperatures?

The low latitudes receive direct rays from the sun, so the temperature is higher than the areas of the earth that do not receive direct rays.

13. Which direction does the earth spin in its rotation?

The earth spins from west to east.

14. Explain "land of the midnight sun."

On June 21, which is the summer solstice, the sun's rays are above the horizon in the Arctic for twenty-four hours in the northernmost parts. There is sunshine at midnight in these parts of the Arctic.

Matching:

15. G   16. C   17. B   18. J   19. F

20. D   21. H   22. I   23. A   24. E

Chapter 4 Test Answers   Prime Time Longitude

1. B   2. B   3. C   4. A   5. B   6. D   7. C   8. C   9. B

10. Does the time change along the same meridian of longitude as you move from the Northern to the Southern Hemisphere?
    No.

11. Is the International Date Line a straight line? Please explain your answer.
    No, the International Date Line curves to meet the needs of the people that live near it.

12. How many time zones are there in the United States?
    The United States has six time zones.

13. How many time zones are there in Canada?
    Canada has six time zones.

14. Do both countries have the same times? Be specific in your answer.
    Both Canada and the United States have Eastern, Central, Mountain and Pacific Time. Canada also has Atlantic, and a portion of Newfoundland uses time halfway between Atlantic and Greenland Times. The United States also includes Alaska Time and Hawaii-Aleutian Time.

15. What is the purpose of daylight saving time?
    Daylight saving time is an attempt to achieve a greater correlation between daylight hours and the human activity period.

Matching:

16. C   17. E   18. A   19. B   20. D

21. If it is 3:00 P.M. on Monday in Mexico City, Mexico, (99.09° W), what time and day is it in Cairo, Egypt (31.17° E)?
    11:00 p.m., Monday

22. If it is 7:00 A.M. on Friday in Berlin, Germany, (13.28° E) what time is it in New York City, New York (73.58° W)?
    1:00 a.m., Friday

23. If it is 11:00 A.M. on Tuesday in Sydney, Australia, (151.17° E) what time and day is it in Los Angeles, California (118.14° W)?
    5:00 p.m, Monday

24. If it is 10:00 P.M. on Wednesday in Calcutta, India, (88.28° E) what time is it in Moscow, Russia (37.37° E)?
    7:30 p.m, Wednesday

25. How many hours separate Chicago, Illinois, (87.37° W) from New York City, New York (73.58° W)?
    One hour.

26. How many hours separate Dallas, Texas, (96.48° W) from Rome, Italy (12.37° E)?
    Seven hours.

27. How many hours separate Tokyo, Japan, (139.46° E) and Seattle, Washington (122.20° W)?
    Seventeen hours.

28. How many hours difference is there between Los Angeles (118.14° W) and New York City (73.58° W)?
    Three hours.

Chapter 5 Test Answers   Journey to the Center of the Earth (The Lithosphere)

1. C   2. A   3. A   4. C   5. C   6. C   7. B   8. C   9. B   10. D   11. C

12. List the four sections of the earth.
> *The inner core, outer core, mantle and crust.*

13. List two ways we know the interior of the earth is hot.
> *1. Observing molten lava erupting from volcanoes.*
>
> *2. Feeling increasing heat as we go down into a mine.*

14. Why does oceanic crust subduct below continental crust?
> *Because oceanic crust is heavier than continental crust.*

15. What happens when two oceanic plates collide? What can result from this collision?
> *When two oceanic plates collide, the heavier one will subduct. A deep trench forms at the subduction zone. The result can be volcanic activity on the seafloor that will eventually form islands.*

16. List and explain the three ways tectonic plates react when they collide.
> *1) Tectonic plates can converge, which means they come together.*
>
> *2) They can diverge, which means they separate or move apart.*
>
> *3) They can transform or strike-slip, which means the plates slide past each other in opposite directions.*

17. What is the difference between the Mercalli and Richter scales?
> *The Richter scale is an actual measurement of the earth's movement. The Mercalli scale is based on information obtained from the survivors regarding the damage caused.*

Matching:

18. F	19. H	20. D	21. G	22. J	23. B	24. K
25. E	26. A	27. I	28. L	29. C	30. M	31. R
32. Q	33. N	34. O	35. P			

Chapter 6 Test Answers   Mountain Building

1. B   2. B   3. A   4. D   5. B   6. D   7. D   8. C   9. B   10. B

11. What is the difference between a mountain range and a cordillera?

    A cordillera is a system of parallel mountain ranges. Mountain ridges sharing a direction and position make up a mountain range.

12. List and explain the four ways in which mountains are formed.

    1) Mountains can be formed when continental plates are folded, bent, and thrust up as they collide with other plates.

    2) Mountains can be formed by volcanoes that are formed along zones of subduction.

    3) Mountains can be formed when the seafloor spreads, allowing magma to ooze up. The magma will build upon itself until it forms mountains.

    4) Mountains can be formed when a hot spot burns a hole in the lithosphere and magma builds upon itself to form mountains, such as the Hawaiian Islands.

13. List the three kinds of volcanoes and explain how each is formed.

    1) A stratovolcano is formed when rocks, ash, and other debris are thrown into the air and followed by lava flows.

    2) A cinder cone volcano is made from loose pyroclastic materials that are thrown into the air.

    3) A shield volcano is formed by free-flowing lava that flows mostly from hot spots to build up the gently sloping dome of the volcano.

14. What is the difference between a geyser and a hot spring?

    A geyser erupts periodically through a small hole in the earth's crust as the water in the aquifer below heats to the boiling point. A hot spring is a continuously bubbling spring, with the hot water springing from a larger hole in the crust, so there is no eruption.

15. What was the importance of the Cumberland Gap in the Appalachian Mountains?

    It provided a passageway through the Appalachians for Native Americans as well as later settlers such as Daniel Boone.

16. The San Andreas fault divides which two plates?

    The North American plate and the Pacific plate.

17. Why are island arcs found only in oceans?

    Island arcs are formed when oceanic crust subducts and slides into the mantle. The magma creates a series of undersea volcanoes which in time create an island arc.

18. Why do government officials on Montserrat fear volcano education has had a negative effect on safety?

    Because the people now feel they know the volcano so well that they often refuse to heed government warnings about eruptions.

19. What is a seamount? How can it be considered both the beginning and end of an island?

    A seamount is an underwater mountain, rising from the seafloor, that does not break the water surface. If a seamount continues to grow, it may become an island as it breaks the water surface and becomes large enough to stay above the water surface. A seamount could also be a former island that has eroded and is no longer above the water surface

20. Why do the Ural Mountains extend in a N-S direction?

    Because they were formed when the European and Asian plates collided.

Matching:

21. K   22. B   23. A   24. L   25. E   26. H   27. N   28. I

29. D   30. O   31. F   32. M   33. J   34. C   35. G

Chapter 7 Test Answers   The Hydrosphere

1. B   2. B   3. C   4. D   5. B   6. C
7. C   8. D   9. C   10. C   11. A   12. A

13. Explain the water cycle.

> 1) Heat from the sun evaporates water, which turns into a gas (water vapor).
>
> 2) Water vapor collects around particles in the air, forming clouds.
>
> 3) Clouds absorb as much water as possible and then release the water in the form of precipitation.

14. Explain why there are deserts along the western coast of every continent except Europe.

> Trade winds move the warm surface water westward, leaving a void to be filled by the upwelling cold waters rising from the deep. This cold water evaporates slowly, making the winds blowing across it cold and dry. These cold, dry winds do not hold enough moisture to provide adequate moisture for parts of the western coasts of each continent. Thus, these areas become deserts.

15. List the four primary reasons precipitation falls where it does.

> Location, altitude, character of the land, and distance from the sea.

16. Explain why Antarctica is classified as a desert.

> A desert is a region with less than ten inches of precipitation per year and having extremes in temperatures. Thus, Antarctica is a desert completely encircled by currents of extremely cold water, which allow little if any precipitation. Although there is very little new snowfall, the snow that is there does not melt due to the slanted rays of the sun characteristic of high latitude locations.

17. Why are the Appalachian Mountains not considered a continental divide?

> The water that flows down both sides of the Appalachian Mountains eventually ends up in the same body of water, the Atlantic Ocean. To be a continental divide, the waters must flow into separate bodies of water.

18. What must happen in order for glaciers to develop?

> In order for a glacier to develop, there must be more precipitation than evaporation. In other words, there must be more snowfall than evaporation.

19. Explain the adiabatic rate.

> On the average for every 1000-foot increase in elevation there is an equal 3.5°F decrease in temperature as the air expands in the higher elevations. The adiabatic warming is exactly the opposite, with air warming as it descends and contracts.

20. Why is the Humboldt current cold?

> The Humboldt is cold because the water flows northward from Antarctica.

21. How does flooding damage the land? Be specific in your answer.

> Flooding fills the water tables below ground, causing the minerals and pollutants in these aquifers to rise to the surface and poison the ground.

22. Explain why we should all be concerned about agricultural runoff into our rivers.

> Agricultural runoff contains excess fertilizers and pesticides, which are known to cause cancer.

23. Why aren't there any deserts in Europe?

> Because the North Atlantic Drift brings warm waters up from the equator, keeping Europe warm, and Europe is so small there is little land without the moderating influence of water. Also, Europe does not have an eastern coast, it merges with Asia.

24. What does a mean annual precipitation map fail to tell us?

> It fails to tell us whether the precipitation falls in a light drizzle over a long period of time or in heavy rainstorms.

Matching:

25. C   26. F   27. L   28. I   29. J   30. D

31. A   32. G   33. K   34. E   35. O   36. H

37. N   38. P   39. B   40. M   41. Q

Chapter 8 Test Answers   The Atmosphere

1. B   2. A   3. C   4. B   5. C   6. B   7. D   8. C   9. D   10. B

11. Define the adiabatic rate and discuss how it affects air pressure.

The adiabatic rate tells us that for every 1,000-foot increase in elevation, there will be a 3.5°F decrease in temperature. As the temperature drops, the air cools and expands, and the air pressure decreases.

12. What role do the southeast trade winds have in maintaining the Amazon Rain Forest?

As the rain-swollen clouds rise on the continent of South America, they are constantly pushed back into the interior of the Amazon basin by the southeast trade winds, where they drop their moisture once again in the rain forest.

13. List the four layers of the atmosphere in order from the closest to the farthest from the earth's surface. Beside each layer list a distinguishing characteristic of that layer.

1) The troposphere contains almost all the particles and water vapor, which in turn create our weather and climate.

2) The stratosphere is above the troposphere and absorbs harmful radiation.

3) The mesosphere is above the stratosphere and has the lowest temperatures in the atmosphere.

4) The thermosphere is above the mesosphere, absorbs solar radiation, and has the highest temperatures in the atmosphere.

14. Explain the process that creates a monsoon.

During the summer, the land areas are strongly heated by the sun. The air expands and rises, creating a low-pressure area. The oceans are naturally cooler, creating a high-pressure area. The high-pressure area slides in under the low-pressure area, creating the summer monsoons. Coming off the oceans, it brings rain to the continent. The winter monsoon will be exactly the opposite; the land will be cooler than the oceans. Winds will blow from the interior of the continent onto the oceans, bringing cold, dry air.

Matching:

15. H	16. B	17. M	18. F	19. A	20. D	21. L
22. G	23. E	24. K	25. J	26. C	27. I	

Chapter 9 Test Answers   *The Biosphere*

1. C   2. B   3. A   4. B   5. D   6. B   7. D   8. B   9. B   10. A

11. What two things cause materials to decompose more quickly in tropical climates?
    Moisture and warmth speed up decomposition.

12. List and describe each layer of soil.
    The O horizon is the top layer of decomposing vegetation that is found in areas where there is a lot of natural vegetation.

    The A horizon, the topsoil, right below the O horizon, is most important for the growth of vegetation, with a good mixture of organic and inorganic materials.

    The B horizon is mostly composed of inorganic, or rock, material. It may include clay particles that make it dense and thick.

    The C horizon comes next. Here we find rock that is weathering but is not yet small enough to help form soil.

    The R horizon is the solid rock that is the parent material.

13.   List the five major factors that determine the climate of a place.
    1) the latitude
    2) the prevailing winds and rainfall
    3) the location on the continent
    4) the landforms, such as mountains and lakes
    5) the elevation

14. List the four items that plants need to survive.
    Plants need water, soil, carbon dioxide, and sunlight.

15.   Why haven't the forces of erosion worn our planet flat?
    Because plate tectonics continually change the face of the continents, thrusting up huge blocks of crust while causing others to sink, all the while creating new crust.

16.   What conditions must be exactly right for plants to be in a climax community?
    You must have the right vegetation for the amount of moisture, the right number of plants for the size of the area, the right oxygen-carbon dioxide balance, and the right recycling of waste and resources.

Matching:

    17. D   18. H   19. M   20. I   21. B   22. L

    23. E   24. G   25. A   26. K   27. C

    28. O   29. F   30. P   31. J   32. N

Test Scores

Chapter 1 _____   Chapter 6 _____

Chapter 2 _____   Chapter 7 _____

Chapter 3 _____   Chapter 8 _____

Chapter 4 _____   Chapter 9 _____

Chapter 5 _____

Notes

_____

_____

_____

_____

_____

_____

_____

_____

_____